Stationary Steam Engines of Gt Britain
The National Photographic Collection
Volume 1: Yorkshire

George Watkins

The Watkins' Collection in the National Monuments Record

This comprises the photographs and notes George Watkins made during a lifetime of study of the stationary steam engine.

The Steam Engine Record is an annotated set of around 1500 mounted prints of steam engines which Watkins examined in the field between 1930 and 1980. His notebooks contain a record of additional sites for which no photographs were taken, or which comprise written historical notes. In all almost 2000 entries were made in his notebooks. There are also albums of prints arranged by engine type. A catalogue is available.

In addition there are files of notes and other records on all aspects of historical steam technology, the cataloguing of which is in progress.

The main areas of this part of the collection are:

Records of steam engine makers.

Collection of bound trade literature.

Classified collection of data files dealing with, for example, textile mill engines, marine engines.

The collection can be inspected by appointment. Copies of photographs and other documents are readily available.

Please contact:

NMR Enquiry & Research Services
National Monuments Record Centre
Kemble Drive
Swindon
Wilts
SN2 2GZ

STATIONARY STEAM ENGINES OF GREAT BRITAIN

THE NATIONAL PHOTOGRAPHIC COLLECTION

VOLUME 1: YORKSHIRE

George Watkins

Landmark Publishing

Published by
Landmark Publishing Ltd,
Waterloo House, 12 Compton, Ashbourne, Derbyshire DE6 1DA England
Tel: (01335) 347349 Fax: (01335) 347303
e-mail: landmark@clara.net
web site: www.landmarkpublishing.co.uk

ISBN 1 901 522 89 X

British Library Cataloguing in Publication Data: a catalogue record for this book is available from the British Library.

Print: MPG Ltd, Bodmin, Cornwall
Designed by: James Allsopp
Editor: A P Woolrich
Production: C L M Porter

Front cover: Hemsworth Colliery
Back cover: Henry Whitehead & Co, Bradford
Page 3: Rawdon, Briggs Ltd, Ravensthorpe, Dewsbury

CONTENTS

FOREWORD
by A. P. Woolrich

George Watkins (1904-1989) spent most of his working life as a heating engineer and boilerman in Bristol. Starting in the 1930's, in his spare time he made short trips throughout Britain photographing and recording stationary steam engines. In 1965, aged 61, he was appointed a research assistant at the Centre for the Study of the History of Technology at Bath University, under Dr R. A. Buchanan, and was enabled to devote all his time adding to and classifying his collection. He was still making field trips until the late 1970s, when ill health made travelling difficult.

He was an occasional contributor to *Model Engineer,* and other periodicals and wrote important papers for the *Transactions of the Newcomen Society.* Following his appointment to Bath University he was in much demand as a lecturer and produced a series of books based on his research. These were:

The Stationary Steam Engine (1968)
The Textile Mill Engine, 2 vol (1970,1971), 2ed, (1999)
Man and the Steam Engine, (1975), 2 imp (1978) (with R. A. Buchanan)
The Industrial Archaeology of the Steam Engine, (1976) (with R. A. Buchanan)
The Steam Engine in Industry 2 vol, (1978, 1979)

On his death in February 1989 his collection was gifted to the Royal Commission on the Historical Monuments of England. It may be freely consulted at the English Heritage Record Centre at Swindon. As well as photographs the collection comprises numerous technical notes about all manner of steam-engine related topics; an incomparable archive of trade catalogues, some dating from the late nineteenth century; a collection of letters from like-minded friends, of value today for the light they shed on the history of the growth of Industrial Archaeology; lecture notes and slides. His library was left to Bath University.

He would visit a site and take illustrated notes and photographs, usually around half a dozen. His notes usually contained measured sketches of the machines and also the layouts of the premises he visited. In all, he travelled over 120,000 miles and visited nearly 2000 sites, but in approximately 10% only took written notes. Between 1965-1971 he made a selection of the best prints and Bath University staff printed these to a larger format. These were drymounted on card and annotated, and today form what is known at the Steam Engine Record. It is this collection, with notes, which forms the basis of the present series of regional books.

Sites for which no photographs exist are omitted from this book.

The Steam Engine Record is filed in numerical order, but catalogues are available listing makers, engine types and locations. When the field trips were being made the historic county names still applied, but the modern catalogues in the Search Room at Swindon allow searching by new counties and metropolitan areas, such as Cleveland and Greater Manchester. In this series, however, the historical county names have been retained.

When he began his surveys, he travelled by bicycle and train, and many were to sites he could reach readily from Bristol, but he soon graduated to a series of autocycles, on which he would pack his photographic gear and his clothing. He planned his trips meticulously during the winter months, writing to mill owners to gain permission, and then during the following summer, (when his boiler was shut down for maintenance), having saved up all his available leave time, would then spend two or three weeks on his travels, staying in bed-and-breakfast accommodation, or, as he became more widely known, with friends. During the autumn he would write up his notes, and begin planning the following year's trip.

He was initially interested in beam engines, but soon concentrated on the textile mill engines of mostly Lancashire and Yorkshire. In this he was greatly aided by local experts such as Frank Wightman and Arthur Roberts, who were working in these areas. Later his interest included colliery winding engines, waterworks and marine engines. During the War, when he found difficulty in both travelling far and in getting permission to enter industrial sites, he investigated water-powered sites, such as the Avon Valley brass mills, near Bristol, and the Worcestershire edge tool manufacturing sites. An area of steam technology which did not concern him was the railway locomotive, though he did record a small number of industrial locomotives and traction engines he found on his visits.

His photographs are a unique record of the end of stationary steam power in this country, being made at a time when electrification, nationalisation and trade depression created wholesale changes on the physical structure of the industrial landscape. They are an invaluable resource to our understanding of the reality of industrial activity, and will interest, as well as the technical historian, the local historian and modelmaker. It is good to know they are being published, for this in turn will focus attention on the rest of his reference collection, which deserves to be more widely known and used.

ISSES (The International Stationary Steam Engine Society) is publishing a number of volumes devoted to George Watkins and his work. They will include a short biography, memoirs from several of his friends, a bibliography of his writings and reprints of his articles.

Details may be obtained from:
Mr. John Cooper, 73 Coniston Way, Blossom Hill, Bewdley, Worcestershire, DYl2 2QA Tel: 01299 402946
Email:John.Cooper@isses2.freeserve.co.uk
Web site: www.steamenginesociety.org

The layout of this book follows the same pattern as the publisher's re-issue of *The Textile Mill Engine*, namely a page of three sets of notes followed by three full page photographs illustrating those notes. A little editing has been done to ensure consistency, but the texts are as George Watkins wrote them. It is pointed out, however that they were written over thirty years ago, and were often based on observations made thirty to forty years before that. Many of the sites, if they now exist at all, have been radically altered and very few of the engines and machines he saw now survive. A handful of engines are preserved in museums, such as the Bradford Industrial Museum, and societies such as ISSES and the Northern Mill Engine Society maintain records of engines in private hands.

The sites are in alphabetical order of location, and no attempt has been made to place them by precise grid references. Each entry heading has an illustration number for this volume, the location as recorded on the original record card, and the Steam Engine Record (SER) number. This latter number is the key for accessing the copies of the field notebooks and the files of additional photographs in the National Monuments Record at Swindon.

YORKSHIRE

The majority of the sites recorded relate to woollen and cotton textile manufacture, in the old West Riding of the county, and cover the whole rage of processes from spinning, weaving to dyeing. A sizeable block of sites concerns coal mining and concentrates on engines used in winding and ventilating. Another block concerns iron and steel processing ranging from blast furnace engines to rolling mill engines, and edge tool making by tilt hammers. Minor manufactures included tanning, papermaking and clog making. A number of sites were driven by water-power, including some large diameter wheels.

The sets of other prints relating to each site, in the National Monuments Record, sometimes include exterior shots of buildings, but these were very largely excluded by George Watkins from the selection he made comprising the Steam Engine Record.

The whole range of steam engine configurations is covered; many built by local manufacturers. There were some early beam engines, but the majority were horizontal or vertical engines dating from the last half of the nineteenth and the first third of the twentieth centuries. Many notes record continual improvement of engines with new, more efficient, cylinders. Other notes record engine failures with cracked flywheels and beams. A persistent theme is the modernisation of works with electric drives making steam power obsolete. Another theme is the pride shown by designers and engineers. Some engines, especially major waterworks engines, were riotously ornamented with fancy cast-iron work, picked out in colour - a measure of business pride. The working mill engineers frequently kept the engines in spotless condition, a difficult job where some process industries generated quantities of dust.

George Watkins received much help from his friend Arthur Roberts, of Luddenden Foot, and in the Watkins Collection at Swindon is a copy of a notebook written by Roberts listing brief details of several hundred engines he had examined in the 1920's and 30's. Roberts was also a contributor to the Industrial Monuments Record established in the 1960's by the Council for British Archaeology, and his cards detailing engines surviving in the mid-1960's may be consulted at Swindon.

No scholarly work has yet been published about the histories of the engine-manufacturing firms of Yorkshire, but authoritative notes about many of them can be found in R. A. Buchanan & George Watkins' *Industrial Archaeology of the Steam Engine.* Many of the trade catalogues in the Watkins Collection also contain information about the histories of the various firms.

FURTHER READING:

Colum Giles & Ian H. Goodall, *Yorkshire Textile Mills.1770-1930,* 1992, especially chapter 4

Arnold Throp, *The Last years of Mill Engine Building.* 1993, (JISSES 7), Throp worked for the Bradford engine-builder Cole, Marchant and Morley, first as an apprentice and then as an outside erector and fitter.

TYPES OF STEAM ENGINE

Beam engine, the original form as made by Boulton and Watt. This form owed its existence to the fact that all the earlier steam engines were used for pumping water, the beam forming a convenient means of attachment for the pump rods.

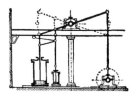

Horizontal Engine, with open frame cast iron bedplate, a type much used for all sizes of engine for general purposes. The bed-plate frame was of a U section, and was bolted down to a foundation of masonry or brickwork, the cylinder, main bearing and guides being bolted to the bed-plate.

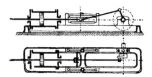

Vertical engine, a type used extensively for both large and small engines; it had the advantage of occupying little floor space. An endless number of varieties of this type was developed, and was the generally accepted type for marine screw-propeller engines.

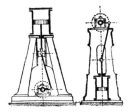

Corliss frame or Girder Engine, a type of horizontal engine. This example had a bored guide, but they were also made with flat-planed guides. In both cases the guides were formed in the main casting or girder which connects the cylinder to the main bearing. There were many varieties of this type.

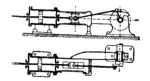

Self contained horizontal engines, with bent or slotted out cranks. This type, largely used for small power short-stroke engines had the cylinder bolted on to the end of an open bedplate, which was widened out at the other end to take both bearings of the crank shaft, so that the flywheel might be keyed on either side. The guides were usually formed in the bedplate, the boring out of the guides and facing of the end flange being done at the same setting.

Oscillating Engines, formerly much used as marine engines. Originally developed for driving paddle wheels, this type has also been used for driving screw propellers. Uncommon in land use.

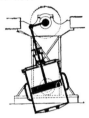

Steeple engine, formerly used for driving paddle wheels. A variety of this type had been used for small powers, and was known as the Table Engine.

Beam Engine, Woolf's Compound. Two unequal cylinders side by side, at one end of the beam. Many pumping engines were of this type.

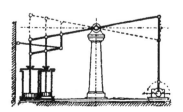

McNaught Compound Beam Engine. This system consisted of a small cylinder (high-pressure cylinder), placed at the opposite end of the beam to the larger cylinder, was introduced by McNaught for increasing the power of existing engines. The high-pressure cylinder was the one added, the original cylinder being the low-pressure cylinder. The power of the engine was thus increased by increase of boiler pressure and the addition of the new small cylinder, to which the boiler was admitted. (See glossary for more details).

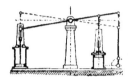

Inclined Frame Engines, used extensively for paddle steamers in several different varieties, usually compound engines.

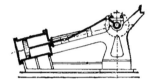

A Double-Cylinder Engine, derived from the above, with the cylinder inclined at an angle of about 45^0, was occasionally used for driving rolling mills in bar iron works.

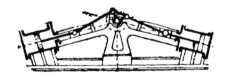

Radial Engines. (Brotherhood type) A recent type, of which there were many varieties, in both 3 and 4 cylinder configurations. These were used for driving fans, steam launches and other applications requiring speed and compactness.

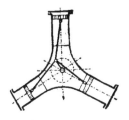

Central Valve Engines (Willans type) A modern design, single acting, compound or triple expansion configuration; a special feature was the hollow piston rod and central valve. Extensively used for driving dynamos coupled direct on to the armature shaft.

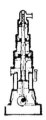

Various ways of arranging cylinders and cranks in double and three-cylinder compound and triple expansion engines

Double cylinder, with cranks at 180^0

Three-cylinder engine, with cranks at 120^0

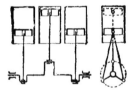

Compound Woolf engine with cranks together

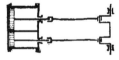

Compound Woolf engine with cranks at 180^0

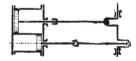

Compound Tandem engine with receiver

Compound engine with cylinders side by side with receiver cranks at 90^0

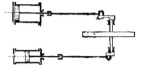

Triple expansion engine with cylinders side by side; cranks at 120^0

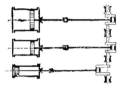

Triple expansion engine, semi-tandem; two cranks at 90^0

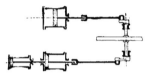

VALVES AND VALVE GEARS

Simple slide valve
This consisted of an inverted metal box sliding on the ported face of the cylinder. It controlled the admission and exhaust of the steam to both ends of the cylinder and exhausted beneath the box valve

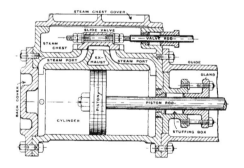

Simple piston valve
This consisted of a turned bobbin, working in a bored liner. It worked on the same principle as the slide valve.

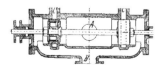

Simple valve gears

These valves were operated by simple eccentric motions of various patterns, and many allowed variable cut-off of the steam as well as reversing.

The Corliss

This was a semi-circular semi-rotating valve working in a bored liner. Separate valves were provided for steam and exhaust at each end of the cylinder, so there were four in number. A trip gear operated the valves.

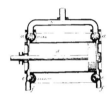

Drop valves

These were circular with taper faces, which fitted upon similar faces fitted to the cylinder. The faces were ground together to make them steam tight. The valves were lifted to admit steam and dropped by the trip gear to cut off the admission. A variety of this pattern was simple bobbins fitted with piston rings.

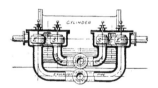

The Uniflow

This had admission valves only since the steam exhausted through a ring of ports in the centre of the cylinder barrel.

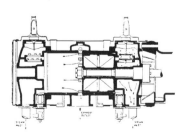

Cornish boilers contained a single flue

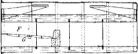

Lancashire boilers contained twin flues

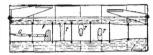

Multitibular boilers were of various types including the locomotive

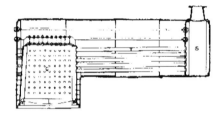

Vertical boilers were of various types. Used in very small plants

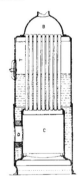

Watertube boilers were of various types.

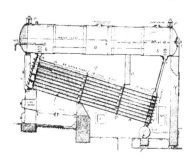

POWER TRANSMISSION

Rope drives, taking power from the engine to the floors of a mill, were usual in textile mills. In older mills power was often transmitted by a vertical shaft.

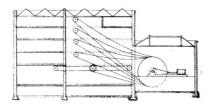

Flat belts of leather or rubberized canvas drove individual machines from a line shaft powered by the rope drive.

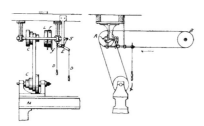

MINING

Winding was done by steam, utilising different types of pithead gear.

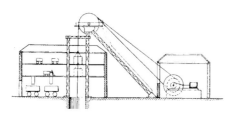

Ventilation was done by various patterns of steam driven rotary fan.

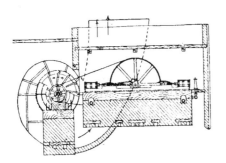

PUMPING

Cornish engines had three valves and were single acting.

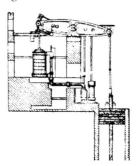

Bull engines differed from the Cornish engine by having the cylinder placed directly over the shaft, the piston rod being coupled directly to the pump rod.

GLOSSARY

Air pump. This removed the condensed water and air contained in the steam. The engine normally drove it itself.

Arbor. An axle or spindle

Condensers. These were airtight chambers into which the exhaust steam passed for cooling back to warm water. Cooling was by a jet of cold water which mixed with the condensate, or, in another pattern of condenser, the cold water passed through a number of small tubes to condense the steam outside them.

Edge tools. These were any kind of hand tool with a sharp cutting edge, such as a spade, hoe, sickle or scythe. A slip of toughened steel was forged as a sandwich between softer metal, and then sharpened. This was an ancient craft, some of the sites utilising water-powered tilt hammers.

Egg-ended boiler. A horizontal cylindrical boiler with hemispherical ends and no flues. At early pattern, superseded by the Cornish and Lancashire types.

Glands. These were recessed bosses in the cylinder cover or valve chest of a steam engine or pump which were fitted with fibre or metal packing. They allowed the rods to work freely without leaking steam or water.

Governor. This device controlled the speed of the engine, if it was too fast or slow, by regulating the steam supply. There were many patterns but all depended on rotating weights, which adjusted the control mechanism.

Grid. The National Grid, the national electricity supply system, was begun in the 1920's. Before it became very widespread by the 1950's, many small towns and larger businesses generated their own supplies, with varying supply standards.

McNaughting was patented by William McNaught of Glasgow in 1845. Piston loads were thus opposed, so reducing stresses on the beam centre. The fitting of high-pressure boilers and compound working gave great economy.

Rastrick Boiler. A pattern of vertical boiler which utilised the waste heat from wrought iron-making processes.

Room and Power. The term means that a capitalist established a factory with a power supply (usually steam), and heating, and rented out space to small craftsmen or manufacturers. Each floor had a drive shaft taken from the engine from which individual machines, owned and worked by the tenants, were driven.

SOURCES

Definitions and illustrations used have been drawn from:

Wilfred Lineham, *A text book of Mechanical Engineering*, 9ed, 1906.

Arnold Lupton, *Mining*, 3ed, 1906.

Herman Haeder and H. H.P. Powles, *Handbook on the Steam Engine*, 4ed, 1914

More detailed technical information about engine design may be found in:

Colin Bowden, 'The stationary steam engine; a critical bibliography', *Industrial Archaeology Review*, XV, (1992-3), pp 177

George Watkins, *The Stationary Steam Engine*, 1968

George Watkins, *The Textile Mill Engine*, 2 vol, 1970, 1971 (reprinted Landmark Publishing, 1 vol, 1999)

R. A. Buchanan & George Watkins, *Man and the Steam Engine*, 1975, 2ed 1978

R. A. Buchanan & George Watkins, *The Industrial Archaeology of the Steam Engine*, (1976) This is a very authoritative account of the evolution of design and construction.

George Watkins. *The Steam Engine in Industry,* 2 vol, (1978, 1978). The linking passages describing the application of steam to different industries are specially valuable.

Transactions of the Newcomen Society, especially: Arnold Throp 'Some notes on the history of the Uniflow Steam Engine, vol 43 (1970-71) pp 19-39

George Watkins, 'The development of the Steam Winding Engine' vol 50, (1978-79), pp 11-24

James I. Wood, 'The introduction of the Corliss Engine into Britain', vol 52, (1980-81) pp 1-13

R. W. M. Clouston, 'The development of the Babcock Boiler in Britain up to 1939, vol 58, (1986-87), pp 75-87

James L. Wood. The Sulzer steam engines comes to Britain, vol 59, (1987-88), pp 129-152

Stationary Power Journals of the International Steam Engine Society, especially: William D. Sawyer, *Corliss Man and engine*, 2 vol, 1994, (JISSES 10), 1997, (JISSES 13)

1 Thomas Ambler & Co., Ardsley Mills, Ardsley   SER 1155

Type:	Horizontal Cross Compound
Photo taken:	1964
Maker and Date:	Hick, Hargreaves, Bolton, 1912. No. 612
Cylinder/dimensions:	20in and 40in x 4ft 0in – Corliss Valves
Hp: 900	*Rpm:* 89 *Psi:* 160
Service:	Woollen Spinning, 22 rope drive to mill. Flywheel about 22ft diameter

The engine cost £1,800 in 1912 and continued to run the mill with overloads for over fifty years. Almost the only alteration was the removal of the original Edwards air pump and the substitution of a Breguet jet air pump which had been provided for an exhaust steam turbine system, which was not completed. Some motor drives were gradually installed as new machines with built-in drives were added, the complete conversion of the mill to electricity being completed by 1966 when the engine was scrapped.

2 Wellhouse Mills, Barnoldswick (now in Lancashire)   SER 1024

Type:	Horizontal Twin Tandem
Photo taken:	1960
Maker and Date:	Burnley Ironworks, 1892 onwards
Cylinder/dimensions:	
Hp: 1100 maximum	*Rpm:* 80 *Psi:* 160
Service:	Cotton Weaving

Wellhouse was a large weaving concern, at one time using nearly 1100 h.p. in three weaving sheds; the whole town was in fact almost entirely weaving, with some of the largest sheds in the trade. Wellhouse was owned by Bracewells, who owned the Burnley Ironworks in the 19th century, and the engine, installed as one side only in 1892, had several alterations and rebuildings following on the addition of the right hand side in 1899. The last major work was the complete replacement of the left hand side in 1925. It continued to run thus, providing room and power until in the 1950s. The drives were changed to electric motors and the engine as seen was dismantled and scrapped when still in good condition. It ran very well although the two sides were never matched in valves or sizes.

3 A & G Carr, Crow Nest Shed, Barnoldswick   SER 1104

Type:	Horizontal Cross Compound – Condensing
Photo taken:	1962
Maker and Date:	Burnley Ironworks, 1914
Cylinder/dimensions:	22in and 42in x 4ft 6in
Hp: 900	*Rpm:* 75 *Psi:* 160
Service:	Cotton Weaving 19 rope drive to main shaft, from 20ft flywheel, 500 looms

This was one of the last engines built at the "Old Shop", and one of their largest. It drove two large weaving sheds, originally by the usual bevel wheels and cross loom shafts, but latterly one shed was converted to electrical drive, possibly with Northrop looms and driven from the engine by an alternator. The plant was a fine example of the latest phase of the Lancashire loom industry, in an area which, although in Yorkshire, once had almost as great a concentration of looms as anywhere in the cotton trade. It closed in the 1960s.

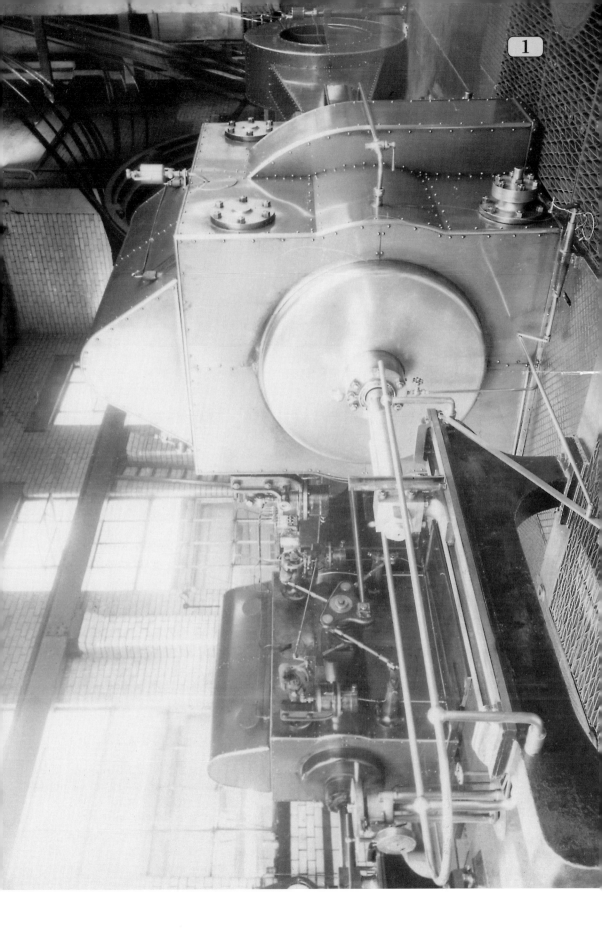

3

4 *Nutter & Co., Bancroft Shed, Barnoldswick*   SER 1186a

Type:	Horizontal Cross Compound
Photo taken:	1965
Maker and Date:	Wm. Roberts, Nelson, 1914
Cylinder/dimensions:	Abt 16in and 32in x 4ft 0in – Corliss Valves
Hp: 600	*Rpm:* 68 *Psi:* 160
Service:	Cotton Weaving, 13 rope drive off 16ft 6in flywheel, 1100 looms once.

Nutters is the last large shed on steam drive in an area that was once a leading weaving district, probably with twenty steam engines in the early 1900s. Nutters was possibly the last new shed to be built there, and too, possibly Roberts' last large new engine. There is a single Hewett and Kellett boiler of 1919 which could suggest that the plant may not have started work until then. A part of the load is now from a 125 KW alternator, and some Northrop looms. A Lumb's governor has been fitted; the connecting rod has not the raised centre boss which was characteristic of Roberts' design for many years. The plant was running and no alteration was considered when seen in 1971.

5 *Nutter & Co., Bancroft Shed, Barnoldswick*   SER1186b

Type:	Horizontal Single Cylinder Non-Condensing
Photo taken:	1965
Maker and Date:	Brown, Son & Pickles, 1914
Cylinder/dimensions:	8in x 1ft 0in – Slide Valve
Hp: 10	*Rpm:* 120 *Psi:* 60-80
Service:	Donkey engine for yarn size coating plant, usually called "Taping", 6in belt drive.

The warp threads, i.e. those which ran lengthwise through the cloth, had to take most of the strain in weaving and in use, and were much stronger than the cross or weft threads. The warp yarns were coated with a mixture of flour and glue to add to their resistance to damage by the reed, shuttle and batting stick movements in weaving. Taping, as this was termed, was done on a separate machine, which could not be stopped until the beam of yarns was completely "sized". Taping therefore could not stop when the main engine was stopped at dinner time, and these taping "donkeys", as they were termed, were always provided to keep the taping going when the engine stopped. Every shed that did its own taping (as indeed most did) had a donkey, almost a standard design similar to this.

6 *The Moss Shed Co., Barnoldswick*   SER 790

Type:	Horizontal, Twin Tandem – Condensing
Photo taken:	1956
Maker and Date:	The Burnley Ironworks Co., 1903
Cylinder/dimensions:	17in and 32in x 4ft 0in – Corliss Valve
Hp: 1000	*Rpm:* 72 *Psi:* 160
Service:	Cotton Weaving

This, as long as trade was good, had always been fully loaded. It worked this way for probably one half of its life. The area was long noted for the large weaving sheds and many looms it contained, weaving probably providing 75% of the employment. The trade suffered badly from cheap imported cloth, and most of the weaving had vanished by the mid 1960s with possibly 3 out of some 20 sheds only still at work. Moss closed about 1960 and all was scrapped.

7 North Gawber Colliery, Nr. Barnsley   SER 359

Type:	Non-Condensing Bull
Photo taken:	1950
Maker and Date:	Maker Unknown, 1852
Cylinder/dimensions:	45in x 5ft 6in – Cornish Valves
Hp: ?	*Rpm:* 9-12 *Psi:* 40
Service:	Mine pump. Pump data unknown

The cast iron plate states "T. N. G. B. I. C. S. Gazette Extraordinary 1852", but very little was known of the engine or the plate on the side as the engine had been disused for many years. There were two Cornish boilers, about 6'9" x 27'0" – by different makers, but as the engine was only a little-used standby, working conditions are not known. The upper part of the cylinder was connected to a pipe to the atmosphere, and the exhaust steam was delivered to a tank from which the feed water was taken, the boiler feed being nearly boiling. The colliery was probably closed in the 1950s, but amid so much change a positive pattern could not be established.

"T.N.G.B." in the above plate stands for "This name given by" I.C.S., but latterly no-one knew who I.C.S. was.

8 The Wharncliffe Silkstone Colliery, Nr Barnsley   SER 626

Type:	Single Cylinder Vertical – Non-Condensing
Photo taken:	1954
Maker and Date:	A & G Davies, Tipton, Staffordshire, 1855
Cylinder/dimensions:	30in x 5ft 6in – Drop Valves
Hp:	*Rpm:* *Psi:*
Service:	Coal winding. Shaft depth unknown. Closed 1950s.

A neat engine with good arabesque moulding in the framings this had been, and still was, heavily loaded in the 1950s. A separate plug rod was fitted to drive the valves in each direction, the engine being reversed by a lever which was moved horizontally to engage in the correct catches on the plug rods, but the valves were often hand operated by keeping the lever in the middle, i.e. between the two sets of catches, as the driver is doing in the photograph. This was often done with short winds of 10-15 revolutions of the engine, in shallow shafts.

9 Frickley Main Colliery, Nr Barnsley   SER 630

Type:	Horizontal Twin Cylinder
Photo taken:	1954
Maker and Date:	Markham & Co., Chesterfield, 1904
Cylinder/dimensions:	48in x 7ft 6in – Drop Valves
Hp: 1,000	*Rpm:* 30 *Psi:* 160
Service:	Coal winding. Rope drum 25ft diameter.

This was of the half a dozen most powerful winding engines made for the intensive deep working of the Yorkshire Main hard coals. It was certainly worked hard, the colliery probably turning nearly 20,000 tons per week at full production. There was an extensive exhaust steam utilization system in the 1920s, when the large amounts of exhaust steam would produce up to 3,000 KW per hour. The whole was turned over to electrical operation in the 1960s.

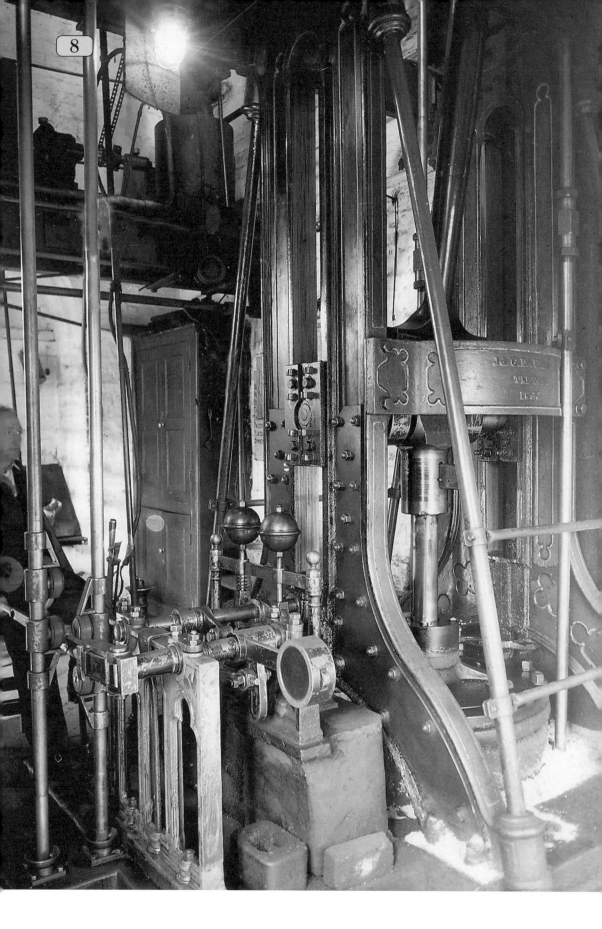

9

10 Crabtree & Co., Carr Top Mills, Batley   SER 111

Type:	Single Cylinder Beam
Photo taken:	1935
Maker and Date:	J & J Horsfield, Dewsfield, ?1868
Cylinder/dimensions:	30in x 5ft 0in – Slide View
Hp:	*Rpm:* *Psi:*
Service:	Woollen Spinning Geared main drive. Belts to some floors.
Beam:	15ft 0in long. Flywheel 18ft 0in diameter

J & J Horsfield were well known as boiler makers, but no record of any engine work by them remained in their office in 1950. This engine had the name and date clearly moulded on the valve chest, and the crank web had a curious hump shape which I met on another engine upon which they were said to have done work. The whole was unaltered, retaining the cast iron connecting rod, the flywheel with the hub side plates, eyebolts to hold the gland, lattice eccentric rod, and the long "D" slide valve, all features of the early 19th century. The works closed in 1939.

11 Abraham Day & Co., Albion Mill, Batley Carr   SER 152a

Type:	Single Cylinder Beam
Photo taken:	1934
Maker and Date:	Unknown, c.1860?
Cylinder/dimensions:	36in x 6ft 0in ? – SlideValve. Beam: 18ft 0in long. Flywheel: 22ft 0in diamter.
Hp:	*Rpm:* *Psi:*
Service:	Woollen Mill. Spur gear drive to mill shaft.

This was a slightly built engine, that drove the plant for over 70 years unaltered. There was no nameplate, and the scalloped finish to the bottom of the main links of the parallel motion were unlike any known make. My hurried unauthorised visit allowed little but a photograph to be taken, and the engine was probably taken out soon after. The works was closed c 1940.

12 Alfred Barker & Co., Wadworth Mill, Todmorden   SER 152b

Type:	McNaughted Single Beam
Photo taken:	1935
Maker and Date:	Unknown
Cylinder/dimensions:	Sizes Unknown. Slide Valves
Hp:	*Rpm:* *Psi:*
Service:	Cotton doubling, gear drive off toothed ring on flywheel arms.

Again an unauthorized visit made when the mill was being scrapped, nothing could be traced of the engine. The stairway castings, and parts of the governor suggests Petrie's work, but so much was gone that it is only guesswork.

13 John White & Co., Leather Tanners, Bingley   SER 1151

Type:	Horizontal Single Cylinder. Non-Condensing
Photo taken:	1964
Maker and Date:	Carr, Foster & Co., Bingley, c.1900
Cylinder/dimensions:	15 $^1/_4$in x 2ft 6in – Slide Valve
Hp: 120	*Rpm:* 90 *Psi:* 100
Service:	Plant drive by belt 12in wide.

Carr Fosters made only slide valve engines, mostly single cylinder, and mostly used in the local mills. They may have made two or three compound engines, but none over 200 hp. They were usually governed by cut-off under governor control, with a triangular back cut-off valve, which like the main valve was traversed by a fixed travel eccentric. The cut-off was controlled by raising or lowering the back cut off valve to alter the point at which the inclined ports opened and closed the steam entry. It was replaced by electric drives about 1971, and is preserved in the Bradford Moorside Industrial Museum.

14 Crabtree & Co., The Paper Mills, Bingley   SER 1166a

Type:	Horizontal Single Tandem – Condensing
Photo taken:	1964
Maker and Date:	Carr, Foster & Co., Bingley, c.1880s
Cylinder/dimensions:	13in and 26in x 3ft 0in – Slide Valves
Hp: 150	*Rpm:* 75 *Psi:* 90
Service:	Paper beating machine drive.

This engine was known to have run for 120 hours per week for over 67 years, and was certainly working at the site before that, although possibly it was not a paper mill then. It is probable that the metallic gland packing boxes were a later addition. The high pressure cylinder was fitted with a riding type cut-off valve on the back of the main one, similar to SER 1151. The engine bed was nearly 26 feet long and made in two sections, the six arm flywheel was in two parts and throughout, the engine was as simple as possible. It was regrettable that a fire completely wrecked the mill in the later 1960s and the building floors collapsed onto the engine which fell below, and the mill was abandoned. The paper machine SER 1166b was also buried.

15 Crabtree & Co., The Paper Mills, Bingley   SER 1166b

Type:	Horizontal Single Cylinder – Non-Condensing
Photo taken:	1964
Maker and Date:	Maker Unknown, c.1874
Cylinder/dimensions:	10in x 1ft 6in – Slide Valve
Hp: 10	*Rpm:* 80 *Psi:* 80
Service:	Paper making machine drive by gearing and by 9in belt to the dry end of the machine.

This was probably supplied with the paper making machine, which had been much altered and added to. It probably dated from 1874, the date of the earliest part of the machine, i.e. drums marked "Redfern, Smith and Law, Bury, 1874". The design was very old, as was the massive ashlar stone base on which it stood. The exhaust went to the drying cylinders, and there was absolutely nothing that could have been left off it. The metallic piston rod packing was an addition, and the piston rod guide had been renewed. The engine, like the beater engine 1166a is also buried in the ruins of the mill.

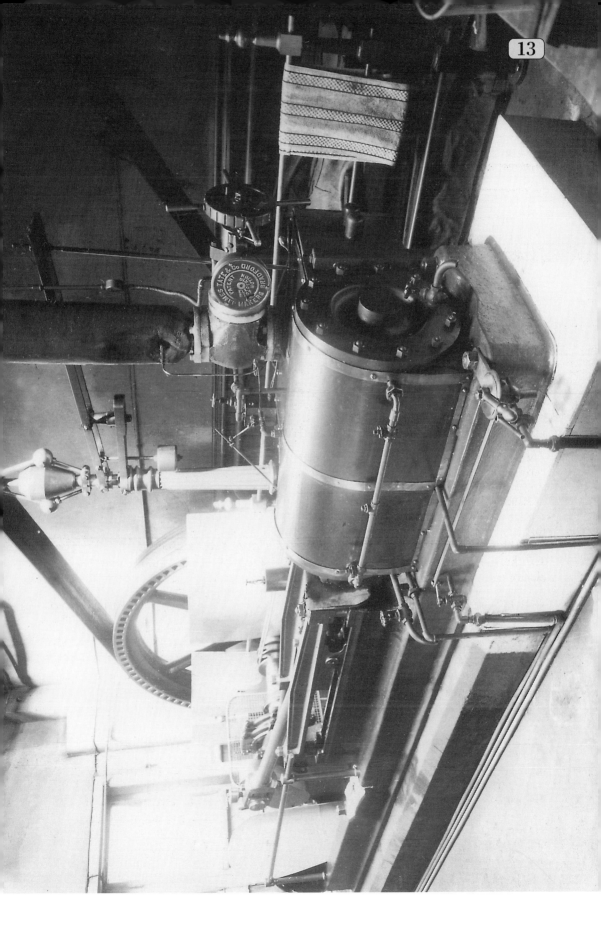

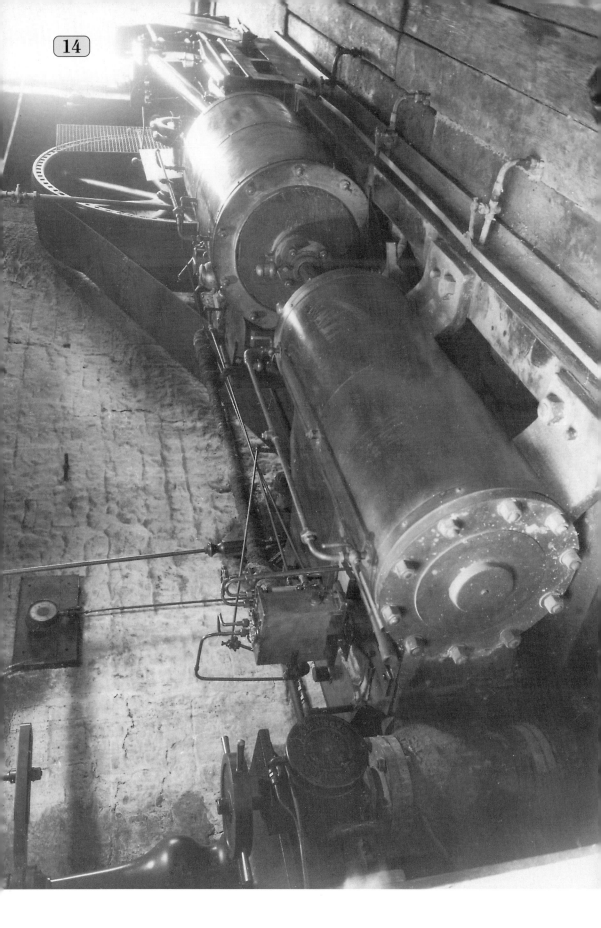

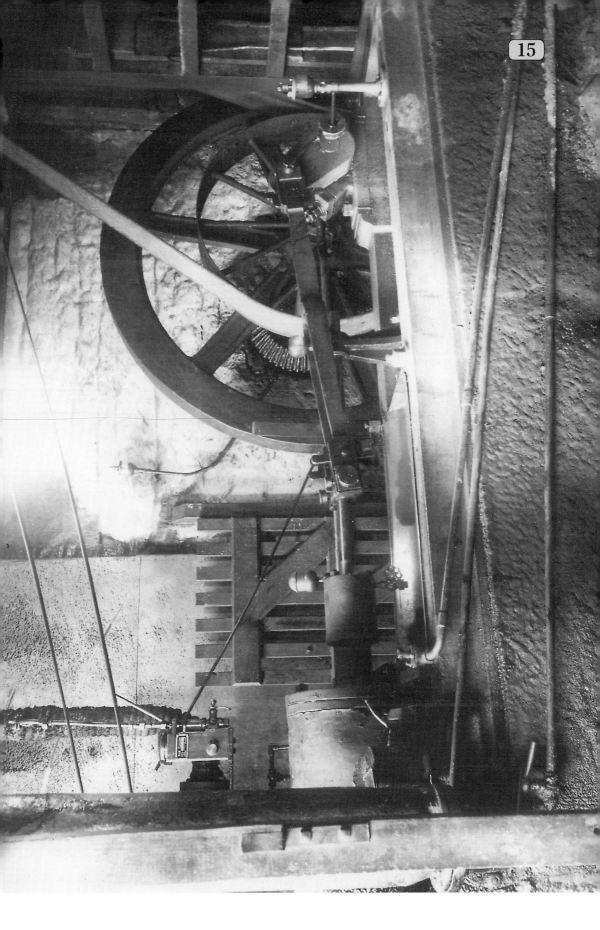

16 George Blackburn & Co., Providence Mill, Birstall   SER 1138

Type:	Single Cylinder Horizontal – Condensing
Photo taken:	1963
Maker and Date:	Mark Shaw, Milnsbridge, 1904
Cylinder/dimensions:	18in x 3ft 0in – Corliss Valves
Hp: 150	*Rpm:* 78 *Psi:* 100
Service:	Woollen cloth manufacturers. 7 rope drive off 12ft flywheel.

This was an old plant and certainly had a beam engine once, gear driving the whole by a shaft underneath the entire mill, and there had no doubt been fulling stocks as well. The underground shaft was driven from that overhead, by a rope pulley on the other side of the wall. The Corliss valve trip gear was the same as Spencer Inglis, but driven from a sliding block, and was horizontal, not the diagonal type wrist plate. The water tank on the roof was by Bagshaws of Batley (1878). The boiler was secondhand (although almost new) in 1933, and allowed 150psi although the engine needed only l00psi. Mark Shaws was a small local foundry, but managed to do quite large work with limited facilities, and certainly made a number of the vertical crank overhead engines used in the Yorkshire mills. The little mill was closed in the late 1960s and all was scrapped.

17 Mathew Walker & Co., Alverthorpe, Nr. Bradford   SER 1058

Type:	Weaving Shed Layout
Photo taken:	1961
Service:	Woollen spinning and weaving

The engine was a Pollit and Wigzell of 750 hp – 1912 cross compound, and driven by ropes everywhere, including the shed type building at the rear. This was later converted for spinning with electrically driven units as seen, but it was partly weaving to the end. Some of the looms were still driven by belts from the rope driven loom shafts, but there were also some electrically driven Northrop automatic looms. The mill was to be closed and all sold in the early 1960s, when much of the modern machinery was sold for use elsewhere. The photograph shows some of the rope drives between the loom shafts originally driving in the shed, which was very well lighted, and possibly built in the 1900s.

18 Leggott & Co., East Parade, Bradford   SER 1087

Type:	Horizontal Single Crank Tandem
Photo taken:	1962
Maker and Date:	Pollit & Wigzell, 1898
Cylinder/dimensions:	9in and 18in x 2ft 0in – Slide Valves
Hp: approx. 600	*Rpm:* 100 *Psi:* 100
Service:	Metal fittings for the building trade. 7 ropes to floor shaft.

This was the smallest engine of the three piston rod type listed by Pollit and Wigzell, and it had remained unaltered for 65 years, with very little trouble or repairs. It was only superseded by electric motors when the Spurr Inman Cornish boiler, new with the engine, had been progressively reduced from 100 to 60 psi, which was not sufficient to run the machinery. The engine was still in fine condition. The Rider type semi-circular cut-off valve on the back of the high pressure cylinder main valve was under control of the governor, giving constant speed despite the variable loads. The whole engine including the condenser, was placed upon a single cast iron bed, and this with the good workmanship in general made one of the best small power plants possible. The simple and direct connection of the governor to the cut off valve spindle can be seen, with a toothed rack to turn the valve.

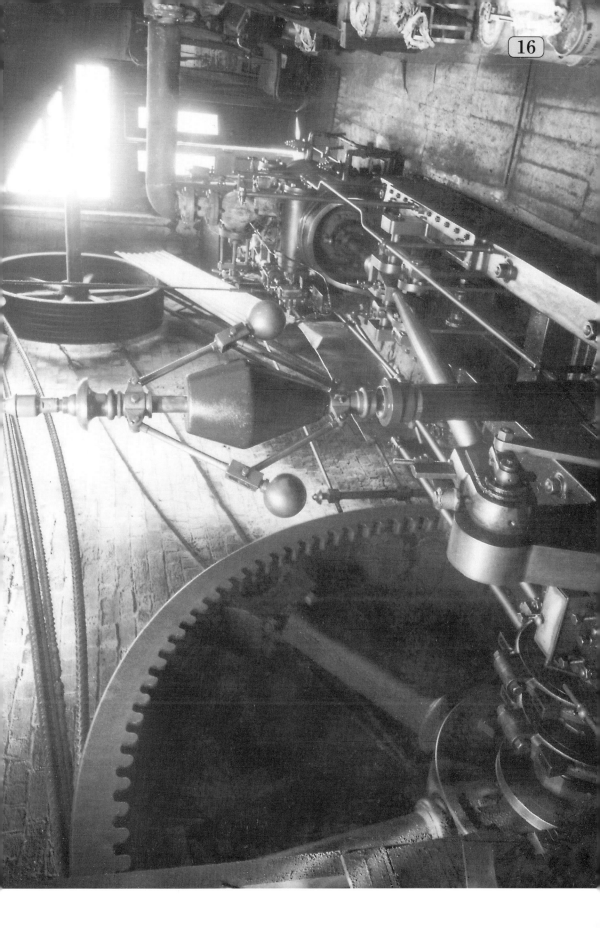

19 Wm. Briggs & Co., Beck Mills, Clayton, Bradford   SER 1108

Type:	Horizontal Cross Compound
Photo taken:	1962
Maker and Date:	W & J Yates, 1880
Cylinder/dimensions:	Approx. 16in and 30in x 4ft 0in – Corliss and Slide Valves
Hp: 400	*Rpm:* 80 *Psi:* 120
Service:	Woollen spinning 10 rope drive off 20ft flywheel.

The mill was built about 1830, with a beam engine and a very fine octagonal brick chimney. The load grew and the beam engine became overloaded. Later it was McNaught compounded, but this was replaced, as the load grew again, with the Yates horizontal engine. This was later altered by the fitting of a new Corliss valve high pressure cylinder made by T. Metcalfe of Bradford. The governing was poor with this and later Newton, Bean and Mitchell fitted their valve gear to it and this, with the addition of a Lumb's governor, ran the mill until it was closed in the poor trade of the 1960s, when all was sold and scrapped. The Yates low pressure cylinder of 1880 was used to the end, still with its mahogany lagging.

20 A & S Whitehead, Girlington Shed, Thornton Road, Bradford   SER 1110

Type:	Two Single Cylinder, Condensing Horizontal
Photo taken:	1962
Maker and Date:	Brearley & Co., Bingley, c.1900
Cylinder/dimensions:	12in x 2ft 6in – Corliss Valves.
Hp: 120	*Rpm:* 101 *Psi:* 160
Service:	Wool preparation, 12in belt to shafts.

These were fully loaded, and were rare in using high pressure steam in simple expansion condensing cylinders. An independent jet condenser with a cooling tower was installed outside the engine room. The plant certainly ran well, with a single boiler by Hewett and Kellett, Bradford, which, second hand in 1914, still carried 160 psi in 1962. The engines were probably installed at different dates, as there were small differences in the details, but they were of similar power. Despite the use of such high pressure steam in simple cylinders, the little plant was quite economical, and successful until the plant closed, possibly as a result of extensive redevelopment in the area; plus the contraction of the woollen trade into larger units, reducing the demand for the working of small parcels of wool.

21 W & J Whitehead, New Lane Mills, Laisterdyke, Nr. Bradford   SER 1191

Type:	Horizontal Tandem – Steam Extraction Engine
Photo taken:	1965
Maker and Date:	Sulzer Bros., Winterthur, Switzerland, 1919
Cylinder/dimensions:	24 $^1/_2$in and 37 $^1/_2$in x 2ft 11$^1/_2$in – Drop Valve
Hp: 1600	*Rpm:* 133 *Psi:* 185
Service:	Woollen manufcturer. Shaft and generator drives.

This was the usual extraction design with counterflow high and uniflow low pressure type cylinders, and operated upon superheated steam at 570° F. The engine had remained as built, but the drives were altered in 1936 from mechanical to electric motors. Originally the main shaft had passed through the shed, driving a number of cross shafts from bevel wheels, also with 16 ropes driving to several other shafts. All of this was superseded by the change to electrical driving, through a G.E.C. 1250 KW alternator, driven by 16 ropes from the flywheel, with no shaft drives at all. Woolcombing was a heavy working trade, and the plant was customarily run for 140 hours per week, and this engine certainly did so until the 1960s, with 100% reliability. It was shut down in 1968 when all current was purchased from the Grid, but the engine was not scrapped. It cost £11,200 in 1919.

22 Heys & Co., Brick Lane, Thornton, Bradford   SER 180

Type:	Double McNaughted Beam
Photo taken:	1937
Maker and Date:	Timothy Bates & Co., 1866
Cylinder/dimensions:	31in x 6ft 0in – Slide Valve,1866 21in x 3ft 0in – Corliss, c.1903
Hp:	*Rpm:* *Psi:*
Service:	Woollen spinning. Built as gear drive with vertical shaft and bevel wheels. Converted to belt drive 1900 – 36in belt to second motion shaft.

This was almost certainly built as a twin with Meyer valves, as the glands for the cut-off valves remained, but blanked off. The main structure was little altered when rebuilt probably by Woodhouse & Mitchell in 1903. The Corliss cylinders were certainly of their make and they did much rebuilding about that time. The change to belts was made due to overloading, and failures of the gearing itself. There was a 36 inch wide belt to the new second motion shaft, and from this belts to the floors drove backwards up to the original shafts of the gear drives. There was a 12 inch belt to the second floor, with another 12 inch to the third floor, and this was split to drive the fourth and fifth floors by belts from the third floor shaft. The belts were an immense improvement and ran with little trouble. Motor drives were installed in 1960.

23 E Illingworth & Co., Shelf Mills, Shelf, Nr Bradford   SER 269

Type:	Single McNaught Beam
Photo taken:	1939
Maker and Date:	Low Moor Ironworks, c1870
Cylinder/dimensions:	32 $\frac{1}{2}$in x 6ft 0in – Slide Valve 27in x 3ft 0in – Slide Valve
Hp:?	*Rpm:* 25 *Psi:* 100
Service:	Woollen spinning. Mill drive by spur gears.

This was probably built as a single cylinder, and McNaughted about 1890, since the LP eccentric rod was the old lattice type, whilst the HP one was of the more modern round form. Other than the adding of the HP cylinder, little had been changed until electric drives were installed in the late 1930s. The engine was scrapped in c. 1940.

24 Fosters, Black Dyke Mills, Queensbury, Bradford   SER 270a

Type:	McNaughted Single Beam
Photo taken:	1939
Maker and Date:	John Sturges, Bowling Ironworks, nr Bradford, 1835
Cylinder/dimensions:	
Hp:	*Rpm:* *Psi:*
Service:	Woollen spinning gear drive.

This was the original mill engine of the Foster firm and was retained as a memento, having had the date it was started painted on the entablature. It was unaltered structurally, retaining it was said the original beam and connecting rod. This is likely as the growth of the firm made more power necessary, so the old engine although McNaughted had less work to do, as new sections, with other engines were built. The engine was preserved in the works in 1938.

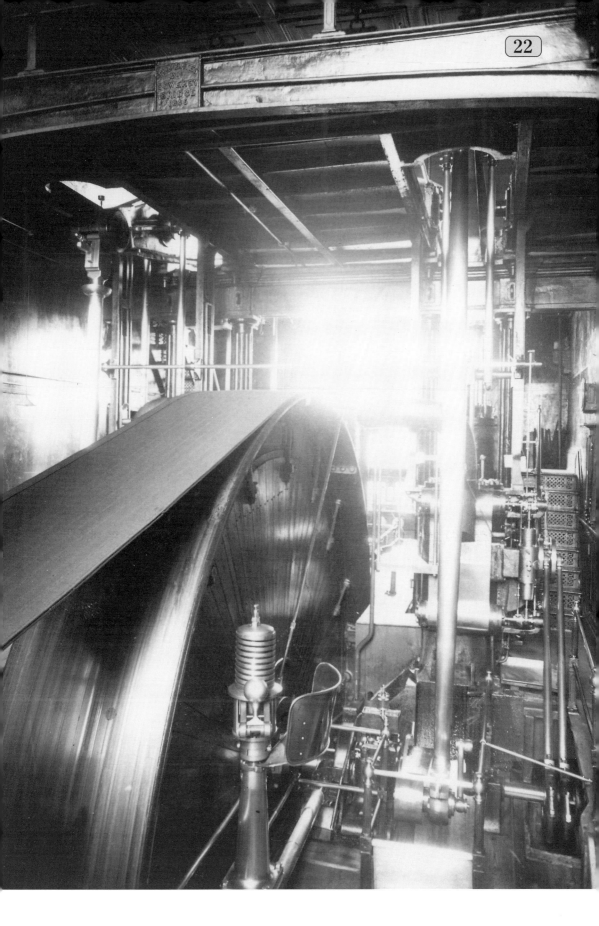

25 Fosters, Black Dyke Mills, Queensbury, Bradford   SER 270b

Type:	Vertical Engines
Photo taken:	1939
Maker and Date:	Unknown
Cylinder/dimensions:	5in x 7 $^1/_2$in stroke – Slide Valve
Hp:	*Rpm:* *Psi:*
Service:	Donkey engines for small powers
	Flywheels: 2ft 6in diameter. Crankshaft: 3ft 6in from floor.

The Yorkshire preference for vertical cylinders was carried into the donkey engines used for driving small sections when the main engine was stopped. The two examples, made by different makers, had been used until electric drives were installed, possibly driving the mechanic's shop, and latterly were stored in the old engine room in 1937.

26 Raistrick & Co., Idle, Nr Bradford   SER 63

Type:	Single Cylinder, Vertical – Condensing
Photo taken:	1936
Maker and Date:	Farland & Brearley, Baildon Green, Shipley, c.1860
Cylinder/dimensions:	18in x 3ft 6in – Slide Valve.
Hp: 60-70	*Rpm:* 60 *Psi:* 70
Service:	Woollen mill. Crankshaft directly connected to mill mainshaft on mill wall with bevel wheels driving 7 cross shafts. Crankshaft 14ft 0in high. Flywheel 14ft 0in diameter.

A plain slide valve engine, this was fitted with a complex governing system with a throttle valve operated by cams. This was replaced by a Lumb governor in 1926. The four fluted columns supported the crankshaft pedestal framing, and the brackets for the parallel motion which was used in place of guide bars for the crosshead.

27 Henry Whitehead & Co., Thornton Road, Bradford   SER 805

Type:	Horizontal Single Tandem Compound
Photo taken:	1956
Maker and Date:	Pollit and Wigzell, Sowerby Bridge, 1894
Cylinder/dimensions:	22in and 42in x 5ft 0in
Hp: 800	*Rpm:* 80 *Psi:* 160
Service:	Woollen spinning. Rope drive. 23 ropes

This possibly remained as built but may have had a Corliss high pressure cylinder fitted in the early 1900s. Little was known of this, but certainly after rebores this high pressure cylinder was replaced in 1953. It had a heavy knock then, possibly due to misalignment, but ran until the mill closed, after family deaths in about 1959, when all was scrapped. The drive had latterly been partly by electric motors, the engine driving an alternator by the ropes going to the rear, but about 15 ropes still drove to the mill. Throughout, the engine was Pollit's standard in details (but the governor was a late addition) and of their three piston rod form.

28 Joseph Sykes & Co., Rock Mills, Brockholes, Nr Holmfirth   SER 1069a

Type:	Double McNaughted Beam
Photo taken:	1961
Maker and Date:	Maker Unknown, c.1870
Cylinder/dimensions:	22in x 2ft 9in and 30in x 5ft 6in each side
Hp: 800	*Rpm:* 52 *Psi:* 120
Service:	Woollen spinning and weaving. Rope and gear drives to mill, shed and dyehouse.

The engine was believed to date from 1870, but the mill was burned out in 1880. The engine room, which was outside of the mill section, was undamaged. It was cotton weaving until then, but was changed to woollens when Jos. Sykes took over and the storied section was built. It was probably McNaughted then, with slide valve high pressure cylinders. The Corliss high pressures were fitted by Schofields and Taylor in 1901 who also then changed the drives from gears to ropes, and reversed the engine rotation. There was a single boiler for 120 psi, by J.J. Horsfield of 1890. The plant and mills had certainly been greatly altered for the better, and with superheated steam was highly economical. However, electrical driving was installed at considerable cost in the 1960s, but the mill closed and all was sold before 1970. The engine had been much overloaded, and the framing had been strengthened in several ways by added stays for the entablature, as well as other points.

29 Joseph Sykes & Co., Rock Mills, Brockholes, Nr Holmfirth   SER 1069b

Type:	Horizontal Single Tandem – Non-Condensing
Photo taken:	1961
Maker and Date:	Ball and Wood, New York, ?1912
Cylinder/dimensions:	11in and 20in x 1ft 2in – Slide and Rocking Valves
Hp: 200	*Rpm:* 200 *Psi:* 120
Service:	Electric light generator and small mill load.

Many local areas did not have public electricity supplies until quite late, and the mills usually installed their own plant. This set was probably bought second hand, as few American units were used in the English mills, and it may have come from a public supply station when superseded. There was a large dynamo driven from the mill shafting, and the Ball and Wood was probably used when the main engine was not working. It was not greatly used in later years, but could provide up to 60 hp for a small section of the mill, by two ropes from the engine crankshaft.

30 Glass Houghton Colliery, Castleford   SER 1222

Type:	Horizontal Cross Compound
Photo taken:	1965
Maker and Date:	Walker Bros., Wigan, c.1918
Cylinder/dimensions:	26in band 39in x 3ft 6in – Corliss Valves
Hp:approx. 600	*Rpm:* 60 *Psi:* 140
Service:	Mine ventilation. 16 rope drive to Walker fan.

Walker's later design, this had been in regular use until electrical driving was installed, but there was also a steam standby fan, a high speed Waddell with a Belliss compound engine connected directly to the fan. All of the engines had exhausted to low pressure turbines in the power house, where there were three mixed pressure turbine alternators and an AEG turbo air compressor, plus a Robey drop valve air compressor. At its busiest, there were 24 Lancashire boilers, but these were changed to water tube boilers in the late 1930s. Much of this nearly new steam plant was soon scrapped on Nationalisation in 1947.

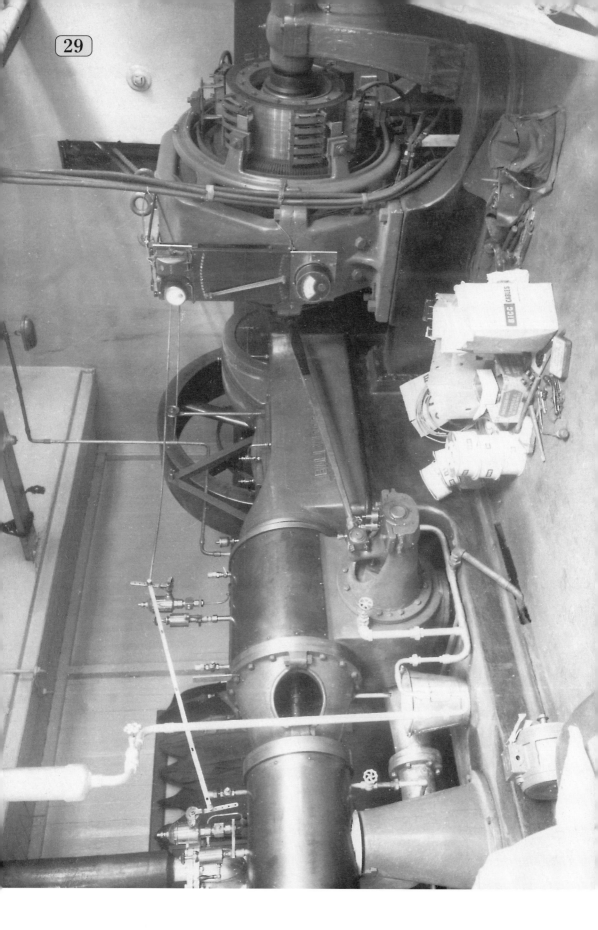

31 Newton, Chambers & Co., Chapeltown, Sheffield   SER 66a

Type:	Inverted Cornish Beam
Photo taken:	1938
Maker and Date:	Newton, Chambers, c.1856
Cylinder/dimensions:	21in bore x 8ft 0in – Drop Valves
Hp:	*Rpm:* *Psi:*
Service:	Colliery pump at Newbegin shaft. Disused after 1926.

This was a rare example of the inverted Cornish design which greatly reduced the cost of the engine house by eliminating the bob or lever wall. The beam was below ground level, with the outer end projecting into the shaft; with the usual Cornish pit work for the pumps. An unusual feature was that the valves were driven from the arbor shaft by eccentrics, instead of the usual wipers, or levers. The general lack of the usual Cornish features suggests that it was, as rumoured, made in the works engineering shops. There had been a condenser, since dimensions were known to exist, but it had long since disappeared. This engine was disconnected and derelict in 1936. It is believed that it was scrapped in c. 1940.

32 Newton, Chambers & Co., Chapeltown, Sheffield   SER 66b

Type:	Beam and Parallel Motion
Photo taken:	1936
Maker and Date:	
Cylinder/dimensions:	
Hp:	*Rpm:* *Psi:*
Service:	
	Beam 21ft 0in long.

The engine was completely inverted. There was no foundation for the cylinder, which was placed upon cast iron beams across the engine house, so that the house cost only a fraction of a Cornish one, merely enclosing the upper parts. The fitting of king and queen posts, with forged iron straps suggests either increased loading or a safety measure after the Hartley colliery disaster of 1862. See also SER 31.

33 Kitson & Co., Denby Dale   SER 694

Type:	Horizontal Single Cylinder – Non-Condensing
Photo taken:	1954
Maker and Date:	W & J Galloway, Manchester, 1890s.
Cylinder/dimensions:	28 x 3ft 0in – Piston Valve
Hp: approx. 200	*Rpm:* 80 *Psi:* 75
Service:	Earthenware pipe and clay products.

This was said to have been removed from a rolling mill in Whitchurch, Shropshire, possibly in the 1920s. The load was very variable, but governing was entirely by cut-off from a radial link and swinging die and valve rod. This was Galloway's usual system for piston valve control for many years, and certainly worked very well here. The engine was substantial and gave little trouble over the years until it was replaced by electric motors in the early 1960s and scrapped. The exhaust steam was used for drying, and steam still had to be supplied for this purpose afterwards, so little was gained by scrapping the engine.

32

34 W H Foster & Son, The New Mill, Denholme, Nr Halifax SER 1086

Type:	Two Horizontal Single Crank Tandem Compound
Photo taken:	1962
Maker and Date:	Pollit and Wigzell, Sowerby Bridge, 1899 and 1904
Cylinder/dimensions:	1899 – 22in and 38in x 5ft 0in, 1904 – 20in and 32in x 5ft 0in
Hp: 700 & 800 resp.	*Rpm:* 80 *Psi:* 160
Service:	Spinning mill drives by belt and alternator.

The two engines were Pollit & Wigzell three piston rod tandem types. The right hand one (1899) drove a 38 inch wide belt to a countershaft, and thence by 12 inch and 18 inch belts to the first and second mill floors. The left hand engine (1904) drove by a belt 38 inch wide to a large pulley and then by a vertical rope driven with 15 ropes to the rest of the first floor. It also drove a 385 KW alternator for various motor drives in the New Mill by another pulley from the crankshaft. The engines ran very quietly with the belt drives, and, together with a similar smaller engine replacing a beam engine in the "Old Mill" and the cross compound for the weaving shed (see SER 366 for this engine), it was a very efficient power system which was run by four boilers in two groups. All was scrapped when the mills closed in the 1960s.

35 David Thos. Lee - Syke Ing Mills, Earlsheaton, Nr Dewsbury SER 1075

Type:	Horizontal Single Tandem – Condensing
Photo taken:	1962
Maker and Date:	Bever & Dorling, Bradford, 1897
Cylinder/dimensions:	18 $\frac{1}{4}$in and 31in x 3ft 0in – Corliss Valve
Hp: 600	*Rpm:* 85 *Psi:* 120
Service:	Wool combing. Also fulling stocks at one time.

This had once been very heavily loaded with fulling and all woollen trade work. It possibly replaced a beam engine installed in 1883 when the mill was built, and was probably in the same engine room. It was very lightly loaded in 1961, as manufacturing had been abandoned, but it was economical still and continued in use in the 1970s. The Bever Dorling valve gear, if not the cylinders also, were replaced by Newton Bean and Mitchell, but the date of this was unknown. The rope drives were fitted to the original gear driven room shafts.

36 Ellis & Co., Saville Street, Dewsbury   SER 109a

Type:	Single Beam Engine with Horizontal Pusher
Photo taken:	1935
Maker and Date:	Beam Engine by Taylor & Hirst, Marsden, 1864
Cylinder/dimensions:	40in x 6ft 6in – Slide Valve
Hp: 500 total	*Rpm:* 24 *Psi:* 100
Service:	Woollen Mill. Gear drives by bevel wheels and vertical shaft.

The beam engine was unaltered during its life, except for the longer crankshaft required to couple the horizontal engine. It was an attractive engine, slender yet well built, with little decoration except for the fluted columns and the single boss in the middle of the connecting rod. The beam was made with a jaw end, with a single bearing at each end of the connecting rod. The drive was by a gearwheel 7 ft diameter, upon the crankshaft, to a pinion 4 ft diameter on the second motion shaft.

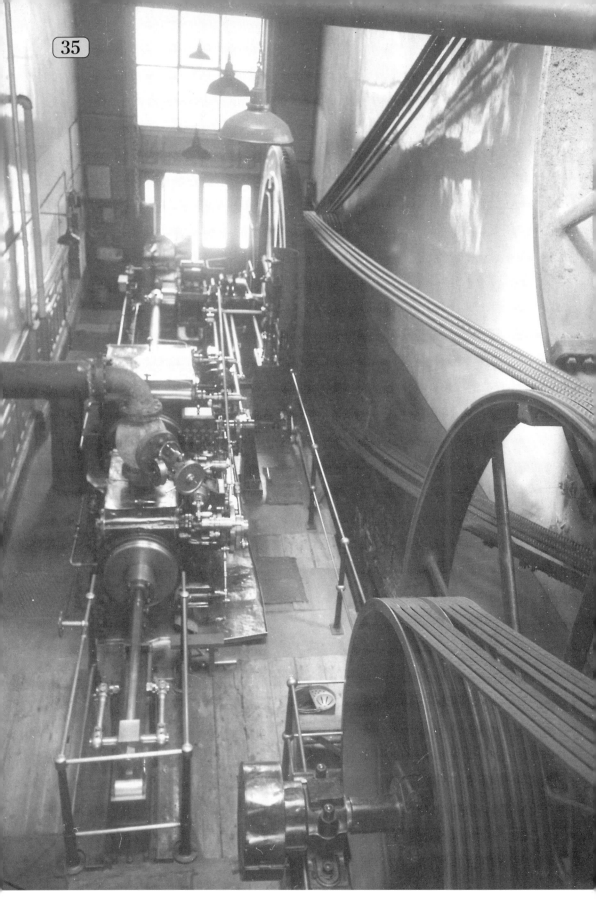

37 Ellis & Co, Saville Street, Dewsbury   SER 109b

Type:	Horizontal Single Cylinder
Photo taken:	1935
Maker and Date:	Unknown, c.1880?
Cylinder/dimensions:	New Corliss Cylinder, 22in x 5ft 0in, 1910
Hp:	*Rpm:* *Psi:*
Service:	Pusher engine.

There was nothing to suggest the maker of the horizontal engine, which had a single slipper crosshead guide, and was built with a slide valve cylinder. The placing of the Corliss valve gear on the outer side of the cylinder, when the new cylinder was fitted, gave a very accessible layout which, exhausting to the original beam engine, was economical.

38 Hemingway & Bindchandler, Church Road, Dewsbury   SER 110

Type:	Single Cylinder Vertical Engine
Photo taken:	1935
Maker and Date:	Wm. Bagshaw, 1871
Cylinder/dimensions:	20in x 3ft 6in – Slide Valve – Condensing
Hp: approx. 120	*Rpm:* 60 *Psi:* 80
Service:	Woollen dyers. Rope drives to dyehouse shafts.
Motion beams:	7ft 6in – long flywheel 13ft 6in diameter.

This was a neat layout in an oak panelled engine room. The crankshaft bearing was supported by two fluted columns, with the cylinder supported below the floor, by lugs on two cast iron cross beams. The crosshead was guided by a grasshopper parallel motion, with its outer end supported by a swinging link, not on a slide, and the parallel rods were supported, one by a fluted column and the other by a crossbar in the main columns. The air pump was driven from the parallel motion beams.

39 Rawdon, Briggs Limited, Ravensthorpe, Dewsbury   SER 1111

Type:	Horizontal Single Tandem
Photo taken:	1962
Maker and Date:	Marsdens Engines, Heckmondwike, 1921
Cylinder/dimensions:	17in and 34 $\frac{1}{2}$in x 3ft 6in – Corliss Valves
Hp: 500	*Rpm:* 83 $\frac{1}{2}$ *Psi:* 160
Service:	Woollen yarn preparation and cloth weaving. Direct drive to mill shaft and alternator.

Marsdens did not make many complete engines after this, possibly a dozen or so, but like all theirs, it was a very good servant. The mill and weaving shed drives were by belts wherever possible, and all of the loom shafts were belt driven. There was not the usual shed mainshaft at the side with its bevel gearing to the loom shafts which was almost standard, and although simple it was very noisy. Some of the blanket looms were very heavy, weaving 50 inch wide. The plant was very well kept, and much gearing had been eliminated when the motors were installed for outlying drives. The plant closed with the general retraction of the trade in the 1960s, and all was scrapped, but it was a very good little plant. It probably had a beam engine at one time.

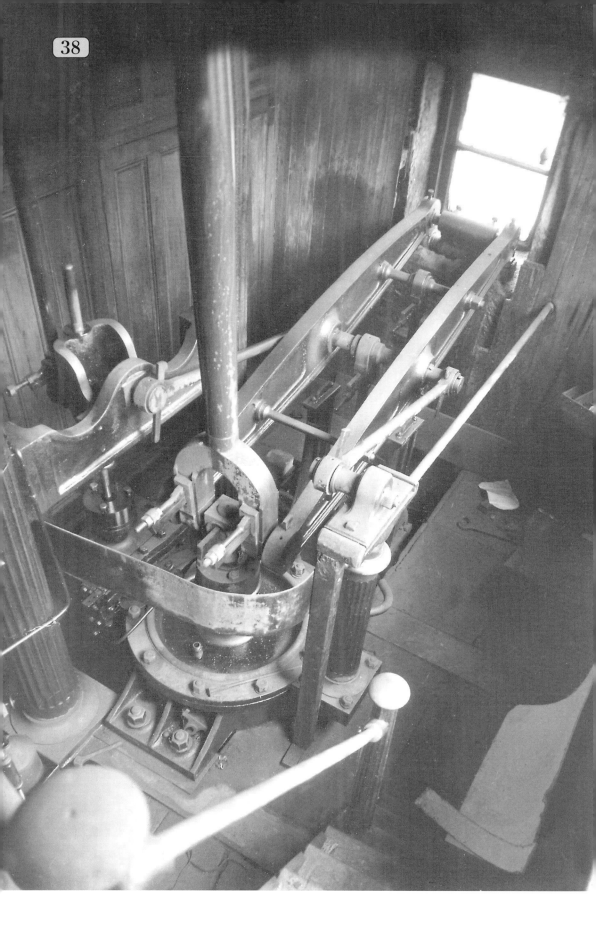

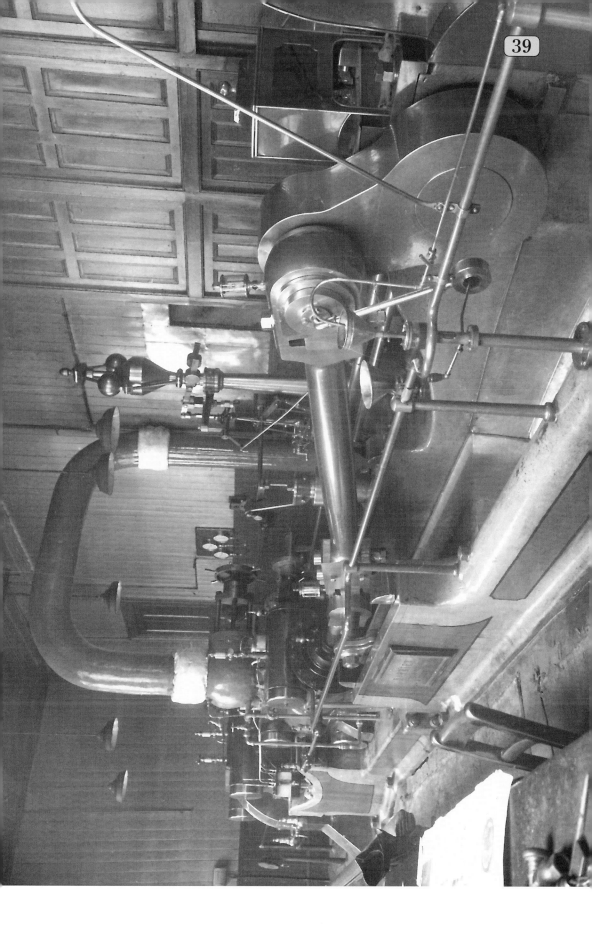

40 Leonard Firth & Co., Textile Finishers, Saville Town, Dewsbury   SER 1342

Type:	Horizontal Single Tandem -- Condensing
Photo taken:	1968
Maker and Date:	Marsden's Engines, Heckmondwike, early 1900s
Cylinder/dimensions:	12in and 20in x 2ft 6in – Corliss and Slide valves
Hp: 150 ?	*Rpm:* 90 *Psi:* 120
Service:	General plant drives. 4 ropes off 9ft 6in flywheel .

The power history was uncertain, there was no portable beam engine house, and this engine was installed secondhand from a closed mill in 1923. The condenser was on floor level, tandem to the low pressure cylinder, and the main driving shaft ran at less than the speed of the engine. Marsden's governors, although very simple seem to have met the needs of the industries, as few were changed to a Lumb governor, and this, too, was unaltered. There was another Firth's works well away from this one, with a high speed compound engine, and the work was concentrated there later. This plant closed and all was sold in 1971. The little engine had more than paid its way in some 70 years of work. Marsden, having a sound design, did not alter it for the smaller powers.

41 Hatfield Colliery, Nr Doncaster, No. 2 Shaft   SER 1428a

Type:	Double Cylinder Horizontal
Photo taken:	1971
Maker and Date:	J Musgrave & Sons, Bolton, 1919
Cylinder/dimensions:	42in x 7ft 0in – Drop Inlet – Corliss Exhaust
Hp: ?	*Rpm:* 40 *Psi:* 160
Service:	Coal winding. Shaft 867 yards deep.
	Rope drum 16ft to 26ft diameter.

This was the largest and last winding engine made by Musgrave's and they only completed 26 other engines before they closed about 1925-6. It was of the Continental design similar to the trunk frame engines they made for India in the 1890s, but with highly efficient drop valve cylinders, able to use the high pressure and temperature steam provided for the power house. It was the main coal drawing engine for this large colliery in 1971 and appeared likely to remain thus. It was very heavily made, with the valve gear on the outer side of the cranks, allowing the main bearings to come close to the rope drum. All of the valves were driven from a wrist plate at the centre of each cylinder, and a piston tail rod was fitted to support the piston weight, on a slide bar. With the conico-cylindrical drum it was a fast engine pulling a heavy payload of coal. The exhaust steam was utilized in a mixed pressure system in the massive power house.

42 Hatfield Colliery, Nr Doncaster   SER 1428b

Type:	Low Pressure Steam Accumulator System
Photo taken:	1971
Service:	Steam storage for mixed pressure turbines.

Hatfield was typical of the latest developments in steam colliery practice, with all the exhaust steam from the very powerful winding engines used in mixed pressure turbines, which, using low pressure steam when available, maintained the power output by high pressure stages. Steam was used directly from the boilers when necessary. The large volume of low pressure steam could not be used directly, it was too great and also varied too much in the volume as the engines stopped and started. To smooth out the great volume initially, the steam was taken first into one large vessel some 32 ft x 9ft which can just be seen across the fronts of the two accumulators in the foreground. The exhaust steam main from one engine can be seen at high level passing from left to right to enter the central vessel which simply contained the volume, and from this the steam passed to four accumulators, the two in the centre foreground and two others on the other side of the central cross vessel. The accumulators contained a large volume of water which alternately absorbed and released the steam, so smoothing out the fluctuations of the low pressure steam supply.

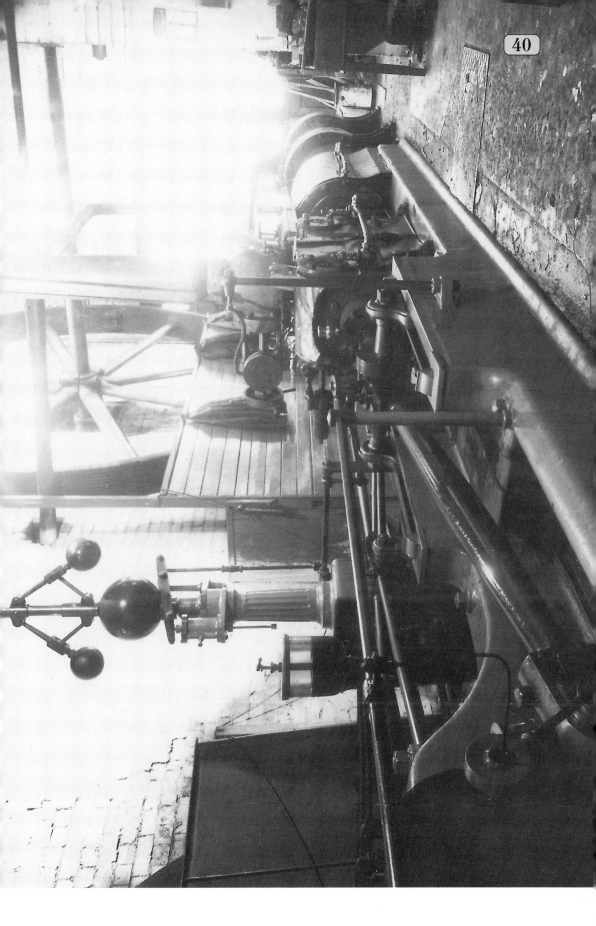

43 Hatfield Colliery, Nr Doncaster   SER 1428c

Type:	Two Turbine Driven Air Compressors and Two Generators
Photo taken:	1971
Maker and Date:	British Thomson-Houston Alternator. 1500 KW (nearest); HP steam, Hick Hargreaves Turbine Driven Air Compressor, 1939 (next); 2,000 hp, Daniel Adamson Turbine Driven Compressor, 1927 (farther end); 2,000 hp, British Thomson-Houston, Generator 1,500 KW (across farther end)
Service:	Power generating house. Supply compressed air and alternating current for colliery use.

There were also at the left two small reciprocating electrically driven compressors. The whole was supplied by 15 boilers. This represents the highest development of the English colliery, designed for high output of Yorkshire Hard Coal in great quantities and from the start to use all the exhaust steam for powering the colliery itself. Such a colliery often supplied electricity to the surrounding villages. Where there was clay on the site, many pits had large brickworks and with coking coal, also had coke ovens and by-product plant.

44 Thorn Colliery, Nr Doncaster, No. 1 Shaft   SER 1429

Type:	Horizontal Twin-Tandem Compounded	
Photo taken:	1971	
Maker and Date:	Fraser & Chalmers, Erith, Kent 1926	
Cylinder/dimensions:	Approx. 35in and 56in x 6ft 0in – Corliss Valves	
Hp: ?	*Rpm:* 30	*Psi:* 160
Service:	Coal winding. 965 yards deep.	

The shafts were sunk in the 1920s, with a double cylinder engine winding from each shaft. The No.1 engine, on the downcast shaft was converted to a tandem compound in 1937 but it was impossible to verify any sizes of the original or the new cylinder layout. It was a highly productive pit, which produced over 1,000,000 tons of coal in 1940, but heavy feeders of water were met soon after that, and becoming steadily worse by 1958, the colliery was then closed, and little used after, although the water difficulty was dealt with. There was a large power house, with low pressure turbines, and a spray cooling system for the condensers, but this was later removed. There were 7 Lancashire boilers latterly, together with two Clarke Woodeson water tube units, and possibly these were additions for the compounding of the No.1 engine and power house; certainly there were several alterations in colliery power stations at that time. Although the colliery is now workable with the water under control, the steam winders are in poor condition and electric winders would be needed.

45 Bentley Colliery, Nr Doncaster, No. 1 Shaft   SER 1430

Type:	Two Cross Compound	
Photo taken:	1971	
Maker and Date:	Fraser & Chalmers, Erith, Kent 1908-9	
Cylinder/dimensions:	Approx. 35in and 56in x 6ft 0in – Corliss Valves	
Hp: ?	*Rpm:* 40	*Psi:* 160
Service:	Coal winding. Shafts 650 and 869 yards deep.	

The engines for the upcast and the downcast shafts were identical, being typical Fraser and Chalmers with cast steel disc cranks, trunk guides, tail rod slides, and Allan link motion. They had been very heavily worked, and were unaltered when at 45 years old in 1952, the saleable output of the colliery was 969,800 tons of coal. The cages were later replaced by 8 ton skips. A complete low pressure steam utilization system was fitted, with mixed pressure steam turbine driven alternators and compressors, and two small standby reciprocating sets. There were over a dozen boilers installed, and in 1971 there were no plans to install electric winding.

46 Askern Colliery, Askern, Nr Doncaster, No. 2 Shaft   SER 1431

Type:	Horizontal Twin Tandem Compound
Photo taken:	1971
Maker and Date:	Yates and Thom. Blackburn, 1911
Cylinder/dimensions:	36in and 60in x 6ft 0in – Corliss Valves
Hp: ?	*Rpm:* 35 *Psi:* 160
Service:	Coal winding shaft 819 yards deep.
	Rope drum 18ft to 30ft diameter.

The two engines at Askern colliery and one at Astley Green (SER 642) were identical, Askern being one of the latest sinkings to mine the Yorkshire Hard deep coals. It was very efficient, with a large power house with mixed pressure turbines for electricity and compressed air production. There are twenty dish-ended Lancashire boilers fitted with chain grate stokers. Originally winding the coal in tubs, these were latterly superseded by a 11 ton skip, with which the wind was made in 50 seconds, and 25 revolutions of the engine. No automatic steam cutoff gear was fitted, steam being kept on for 20 revolutions, but gradually throttled to that point as the speed increased. In later years, much electricity was taken from the National Grid, and only ten of the boilers were in steam at a time, but a large amount of current was still produced on the site. The colliery produced 793,463 tons of saleable coal in 1966, and in 1971 appeared likely to continue unaltered for years ahead.

47 Newton Chambers Ltd., Elsecar Shaft   SER 67b

Type:	Horizontal Return Connecting Rod
Photo taken:	1936
Maker and Date:	Newton Chambers? Date not known
Cylinder/dimensions:	8in x 1ft 0in ? No other data
Hp:	*Rpm:* *Psi:*
Service:	Domestic water pumped from well; geared drive to bell
	crank and wooden pump rods.

This was an unusual design of engine which gave a very long connecting rod in a short space. The crankshaft was placed near to the cylinders, with the connecting rod returning to it along the sides of the cylinder. It was known locally as the Stafford pump, was in the open air and had its own boiler. The engine was scrapped in 1940.

48 Henry Booth & Co., Moorhead Mill, Gildersome   SER 1234

Type:	Horizontal Cross Compound
Photo taken:	1966
Maker and Date:	Woodhouse and Mitchell, Bridghouse, 1899
Cylinder/dimensions:	15in and 27in x 3ft 6in – Corliss Valves
Hp: 375	*Rpm:* 84 *Psi:* 120
Service:	Mill drive. 11 ropes off 14ft flywheel to alternator only later.

The mills were all rope-driven to the several floors until, following a serious fire, only single storied buildings with all motor driven machines were adopted. The engine continued to drive this by an alternator, for a number of years until the engine became disused with the decision to purchase current from the Grid. It was sold for scrap in 1966, just after the photograph was taken. It was a standard Woodhouse engine in every respect and had remained working, almost unaltered except for the drives, for over 65 years.

47

49 Horsfalls Ltd., Ladyship Mills, Glusburn   SER 931

Type:	Horizontal – Cross Compound
Photo taken:	1958
Maker and Date:	Newton, Bean and Mitchell, 1925
Cylinder/dimensions:	27in and 36in x 4ft 0in – Drop Valves
Hp: 1400	*Rpm:* 95 *Psi:* 180
Service:	Woollen manufacture. 16 rope drives to one mill room and alternators.

Like SER 930, this was a modern engine installed to provide for increased loading. However when the mills were extended the added load was electrically driven. It was always very heavily loaded and ran regularly from 6 a.m. to 10 p.m., every day for many years. It was Newton, Bean and Mitchell's latest design, with a uniflow low pressure cylinder, and with piston type exhaust valves to both cylinders. The circular condenser was behind the high pressure cylinder, which was in any case the maker's practice and also there was little room behind the low pressure side. It replaced a Pollit and Wigzell cross compound with all rope drives, and ran with great satisfaction until all of the power load was electrically driven and the current was taken from the Grid. The engine was scrapped.

50 B & H Whitwam, Stanley Mills, Golcar, Nr Huddersfield   SER 275

Type:	Compounded Single Crank Vertical
Photo taken:	1939
Maker and Date:	No sizes or data known – Slide Valves
Cylinder/dimensions:	Crankshaft 12ft 0in from floor – flywheel 18ft 0in diameter
Hp: Approx. 200	*Rpm:* 60 *Psi:* 100
Service:	Woollen Spinning.

This type was very popular in the smaller Yorkshire valley mills, many being made by Mark Shaw of Milnsbridge. It took little space and was accessible and reliable with few repairs. It was also easy to compound, since by the provision of longer side beams for the parallel motion, the high pressure cylinder could be coupled in with a longer stroke. This had been done to this engine and worked very well.

51 Nahums Ltd., Salterhebble, Nr Halifax   SER 105

Type:	Double McNaught Beam
Photo taken:	1935
Maker and Date:	Wood Bros., Sowerby Bridge, 1867
Cylinder/dimensions:	23in x 3ft 0in and 32in x 6ft 0in – Corliss Valves 1902, Beams 19ft 0in long flywheel 18ft diameter
Hp: 600	*Rpm:* 32 *Psi:* 160
Service:	Cotton doublers. Spur toothed gear ring on flywheel arms drove one mill by shaft, and the other by ropes off the second motion.

Each mill originally had its own engine in all probability, and the rearrangement in 1902 increased the power sufficiently to drive both. The engine appeared to have been little altered otherwise. The jaw end to the beam with single connecting rod ends and the neat boss formed in the centre of the connecting rods were features Woods often used, whilst Woodhouse and Mitchell fitted similar slide bar crosshead guides on other beam engine alterations.

52 Maudes, Stainland, Nr Halifax   SER 1059

Type:	Horizontal Cross Compound
Photo taken:	1961
Maker and Date:	Pollit and Wigzell, 1920
Cylinder/dimensions:	18in and 36in x 3ft 6in – Corliss Valves
Hp: 450	*Rpm:* 80 *Psi:* 150
Service:	Mill plant drives from rope driven alternator.

This was one of the last Corliss valves engines made by Pollit & Wigzell, in 1954, and was built for a Dewsbury mill, driving by ropes to the floor shafts. It was purchased by Maudes in 1956 and installed on a small island site in their mill to drive the motors from an alternator. It was moved here by Cole, Marchant and Morley. It was built with piston tail rods and rear slides, but with the condenser below, and driven from the low pressure side crosshead. It was probably one of the last new mill engines houses to be built for a Corliss engine, as well as nearly the last traditional mill engine to be installed. It was a pure Pollit & Wigzell engine of their standard cross compound design, and was still in use in 1973.

53 Calder & Hebble Navigation, Phoebe Lane, Halifax   SER 106a

Type:	Single Condensing Rotative Beam
Photo taken:	1935
Maker and Date:	Unknown, c.1830s
Cylinder/dimensions:	32in x 6ft 0in – Slide Valve
Hp: 50 ?	*Rpm:* 20 *Psi:* 50
Service:	Pump to return water to top lock pound. Pumped 60,000 gallons per hour to a head of 110ft by two 18in bucket pumps driven by wooden rods and bell crank 12 spm.

This was unaltered during a century of work, except that a strengthening girder had been fitted beneath the entablature. The stone engine house with the flywheel recessed into the wall and boarded in with removable board panels in front was a Yorkshire feature often met with in the mill engines. The stone staircase without a handrail and the cast iron grill railings in the front of the upper packing platform plus the cruciform cast iron connecting rod with a circular centre section were all early design features. The engine was scrapped in 1938.

54 Calder & Hebble Navigation, Phoebe Lane, Halifax   SER 106b

Externally the plant was almost unaltered, except that the chimney appeared to have been raised, although even this could be original. Placing the engine above the boiler level was an early feature, there being a dozen steps between the engine and boiler room floors here.

55 Smithsons, Craven Edge Mills, Halifax   SER 108

Type:	McNaughted Single Beam
Photo taken:	1935
Maker and Date:	Unknown – c.1850
Cylinder/dimensions:	19in x 2ft 6in – Corliss Valves, 26in x 5ft 0in – Slide Valve
	Beam approx. 15ft 0in long. Flywheel 15ft 0in
Hp: Approx. 200	*Rpm:* 35 *Psi:* 100
Service:	Woollen spinning. Built as gear drive, altered to belts in
	the 1890s.

A plain industrial engine very little altered except for the addition of the McNaught cylinder. The alterations were specified, as were many such jobs, by Rhodes & Critchley as consultants. The original bevel wheels and vertical shaft were replaced by fitting a flat rim 27 inch wide on the outside of the flywheel rim and driving to the first floor by a 24 inch belt and thence by belts to the upper floors. A single Lancashire boiler provided steam at 100 psi.

56 J Horsfall, Clarence Mill, Halifax   SER 1060

Type:	Horizontal Semi Tandem Triple Expansion
Photo taken:	1961
Maker and Date:	Pollit and Wigzell, Sowerby Bridge, 1894
Cylinder/dimensions:	12 $^3/_4$in; 20in and 32in x 4ft 0in – Corliss and Slide Valves
Hp: Approx. 450	*Rpm:* 86 *Psi:* 120
Service:	Woollen spinning. Main drive by 36in belt to countershaft.
	Most of the machinery in single floor shed type building
	at rear.

This was an early mill triple expansion design, with Corliss valve high and intermediate pressure cylinders on one side, and the slide valve low pressure with the condenser behind on the other crank. In this case, the drive was off to the left hand side which had the two cylinders in tandem, with the low pressure on the right hand side of the photograph, driving to the left by the cross coupling shaft and drag crank system seen at the extreme left side. The whole was highly economical, and it was accepted by the owners that its replacement by electric motors which was carried out in 1961, would give no saving other than the advantage of sectional control of the machines. The engine was the last of several of the type made by Pollit & Wigzell to remain. They built few triple expansion engines.

57 Joseph Speak & Co., Ing Wood Mill, West Vale, Halifax   SER 1088

Type:	Horizontal Single Crank Tandem Compound
Photo taken:	1962
Maker and Date:	Newton, Bean and Mitchell, Bradford, 1911
Cylinder/dimensions:	Approx. 15in and 30in x 4ft 0in – Corliss Valves
Hp: 550	*Rpm:* 85 *Psi:* 160
Service:	Woollen spinning. Rope drives to mill floors.

This was Newton Bean & Mitchell's later standard type, plain, simple and very well finished. The only alteration was probably the Lumb governor fitted in the 1920s. The deep stiff bed plate, with target flanges for the attachment of the cylinders, the circular condense r on the engine bed at the rear, and the neat lagging and guards, were all features of Yorkshire small engine design at its best. This engine had been a very good investment. It probably replaced a beam engine, but it may have been a new mill in 1911. There was one boiler for 160 psi. The mill was closed because of the poor trade of the early 1960s and all was scrapped.

58 Inghams, Prospect Mills, West Vale, Nr Halifax   SER 1089

Type:	Horizontal Single Crank Tandem
Photo taken:	1962
Maker and Date:	Pollit and Wigzell, Sowerby Bridge, 1884 and 1912.
Cylinder/dimensions:	19 $^3/_4$in and 36in – Slide, then Corliss Valve
Hp: 800	*Rpm:* 72 *Psi:* 160
Service:	Woollen spinning. Belt drive to each of four floors.

This always had four belts drive, one to each floor, but it was built with slide valves on both cylinders for 100 psi steam pressure. More power was needed in 1912, and new Corliss valve cylinders were then fitted with two boilers for 160 psi by Umplebys of Cleckheaton. Superheaters for raising the steam to 490° were added in 1957, the cylinders being re-bored in 1954, otherwise little was altered, other than the fitting of a Lumb governor. The flywheel was 9ft wide, and the four belts were 26in; l8in; 18in; and 12in; wide, one to drive each floor from one end of the mill. Electrical driving was installed in about 1970 with a change in management and the engine was probably scrapped soon after.

59 The Spindle Shop, Booth, Nr Halifax   SER 268

Type:	Waterwheel
Photo taken:	1939
Maker and Date:	Unknown
Cylinder/dimensions:	Approx. 12ft 0in diameter x 8ft 0in wide
Hp:	*Rpm:* *Psi:*
Service:	The only works drive until electric motors, c. 1930.

The rather unusual double spur wheel drive suggested that there may have been a larger diameter wheel here at one time, which would then have driven directly to the mill shaft pinion. Nothing could be ascertained of this however, and it is possible that the premises, dated about 1840-45 had been in used otherwise in the early days.

60 W H Foster Ltd., Denholme, Nr Halifax   SER 366a

Type:	Horizontal Cross Compound
Photo taken:	1951
Maker and Date:	Timothy Bates, Sowerby Bridge, 1869
Cylinder/dimensions:	22in and 41in x 5ft 6in
Hp: 600	*Rpm:* 38 *Psi:* 120
Service:	Woollen mill weaving shed drive.

This was built as a twin cylinder slide valve engine and converted to compound by replacing the right hand cylinder with a Pollit & Wigzell Corliss valve one in 1894. It was an interesting engine, having cast iron disc cranks 7'6" diameter, but the right hand disc was replaced by a steel one later. The use of parallel motion to guide the crossheads was unusual, the air pump being originally driven from the parallel motion. Latterly only the left hand condenser was used, but generally the engine was unchanged in nearly a century. Foster's closed in c. 1966.

61 W H Foster Ltd. Denholme, Nr Halifax   SER 366b

Type:	Parallel Motion Guides. Vertical Main Beams 9ft 0in long
Photo taken:	1951
Maker and Date:	
Cylinder/dimensions:	
Hp:	*Rpm:* *Psi:*
Service:	Weaving shed engine.

This consisted of a forged main beam on either side of the crosshead, working upon links at the bottom, parallelism being maintained by radius rods fixed to the bed. It was in fact a grasshopper motion placed vertically, giving a very true motion, and with ample bearings gave little trouble.

62 WH Foster Ltd., Denholme, Nr Halifax   SER 366c

Type:	1951
Photo taken:	
Maker and Date:	
Cylinder/dimensions:	
Hp:	*Rpm:* *Psi:*
Service:	Weaving shed drive.

The drive was by teeth upon the 18ft 6in diameter rim, to a solid pinion 6ft 6in in diameter on the second motion shaft to the shed, driving the 21 loom shafts by bevel gears; there were about 420 looms in all. The flywheel teeth were separate, and joined to the rim by dovetails in slots opposite to each arm. The usual strut between the crank and second motion shafts was fitted. It was undoubtedly the sweetest of all the gear drives, having just a quiet growl only.

63 Standeven & Co., Whiteless Mill, Mytholmroyd, Nr Halfax   SER 367

Type:	McNaughted Single Beam
Photo taken:	1951
Maker and Date:	John Wood & Sons, Sowerby Bridge, 1851
Cylinder/dimensions:	14in x 1ft 9in and 18in x 3ft 0in – Slide Valves
Hp: 80	*Rpm:* 44 *Psi:* 100
Service:	Woollen cloth weaving.

This ran as a single cylinder engine until 1913, when it was converted to McNaught compound by the addition of the high pressure cylinder. A new low pressure cylinder was fitted at the same time, as well as a new boiler for higher pressure, and the gear drive was changed to rope. The little business ran successfully thus re-equipped until the owner's sudden decease in the 1950s, when the business was closed, and all was scrapped. It was a well kept plant, and the photograph indicates how very short a rope drive can be made, when well designed, the pulley and the flywheel nearly touching each other. Although it meant reversing the engine rotation, such a change from gear drive greatly reduced the noise from worn gearing.

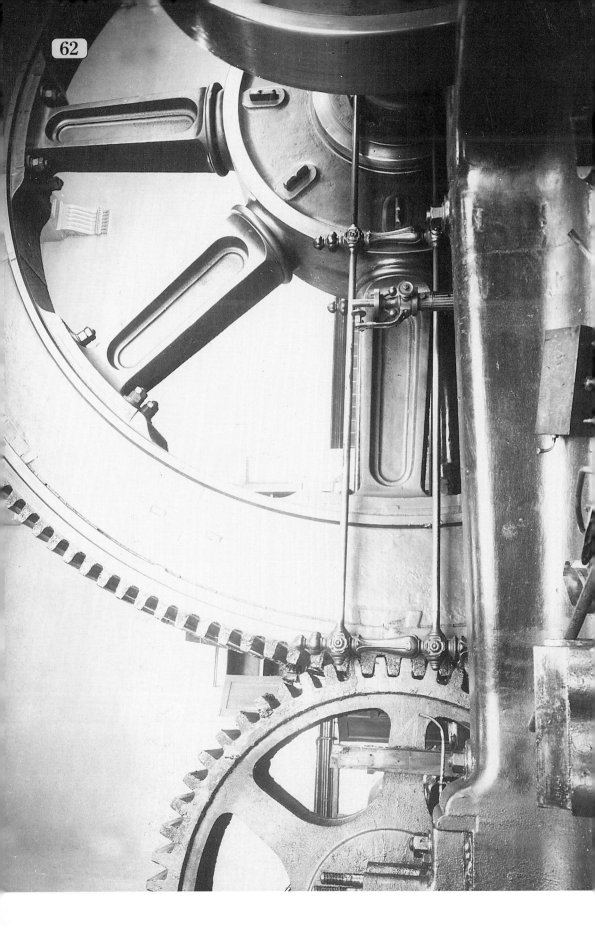

64 Ben Fielding, Woodfield Mill, West Vale, Nr Halifax   SER 381

Type:	Vertical Condensing Single Crank
Photo taken:	1951
Maker and Date:	Wood Bros., Sowerby Bridge, Yorkshire
Cylinder/dimensions:	Approx. 16in x 5ft 3in – Corliss Valves, 1896, Approx. 36in x 4ft 0in – Piston Valve, 1870
Hp:	*Rpm:* *Psi:*
Service:	Woollen mill drive by gears and vertical shaft.

This was a typical Yorkshire vertical single cylinder engine, with Wood Bros patent revolving piston valve fitted to the single cylinder. It was compound converted to compound again by Wood Bros who fitted a Corliss valve high pressure cylinder beside the original one, and longer motion beams to suit. It ran thus until the mill closed possibly in the early 1950s, but remained in position for some years under the new occupiers. Wood's revolving valve comprised a ratchet fitted on the valve stem, which slowly revolved the valve as it ran.

65 Murgatroyds, Oats Royd Mills, Nr Halifax   SER 551

Type:	Horizontal Twin Tandem – Condensing
Photo taken:	1953
Maker and Date:	Wood Bros., Sowerby Bridge, 1895
Cylinder/dimensions:	20 in x 34 in x 4ft 6in each side – Slide Valves
Hp: 800	*Rpm:* 80 *Psi:* 120
Service:	Woollen mill drive.

This was Wood Bros. standard type at the period; plain slide valves, but with a Meyer cut-off valve with a Lumb trip motion under governor control on the high pressure cylinders. There were three engines at the mills all of which were scrapped for electric motor drives in 1956. All of the engines were Wood Bros. slide valve type (Woods also fitted piston valves to their engines). The Lumb trip motion pulled the riding cut-off valve open by the eccentric, but it was released (to close rapidly by a vacuum dash pot) from trips in a sliding block.

66 Skeltons, Holywell Green, Nr Halifax   SER 552

Type:	Single Tandem – Condensing
Photo taken:	1953
Maker and Date:	Pollit & Wigzell, c. late 1880s
Cylinder/dimensions:	Sizes unknown
Hp: Approx. 250	*Rpm:* 84 *Psi:* 100
Service:	Woollen mill drive.

This was a standard three piston rod Pollit & Wigzell engine but unusual in that the mill was driven by bevel wheels directly from the crankshaft, instead of through second motion by spur gearing. It possibly replaced a beam engine which had driven on to the same vertical shaft to the mill floors, but little was known of its history. It was very neat and again unusual in that the low pressure cylinder side piston rods were encased with metal sheeting on the open rod side. A Lumb governor and trip motion were fitted but otherwise the engine had remained unaltered. The mill probably closed in the 1950s.

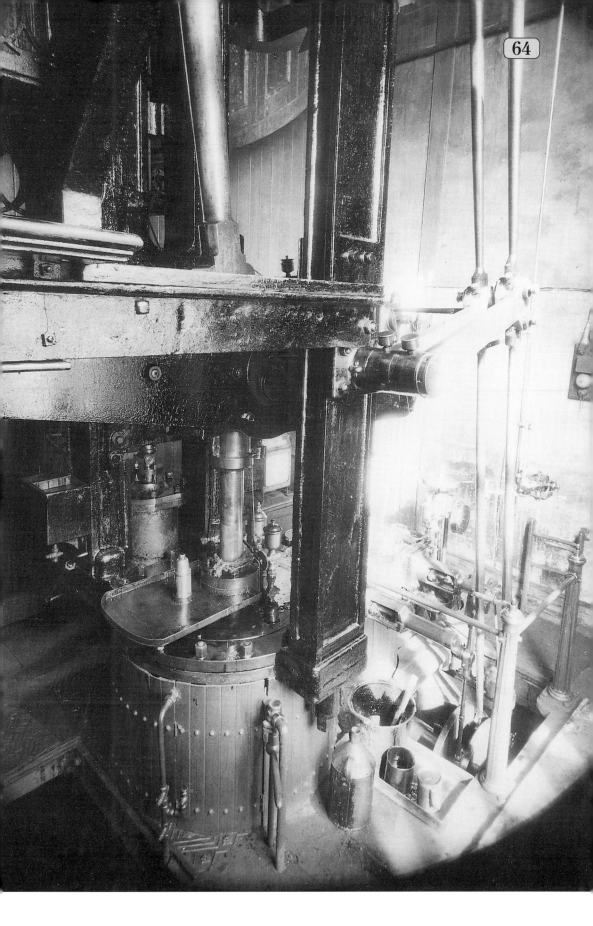

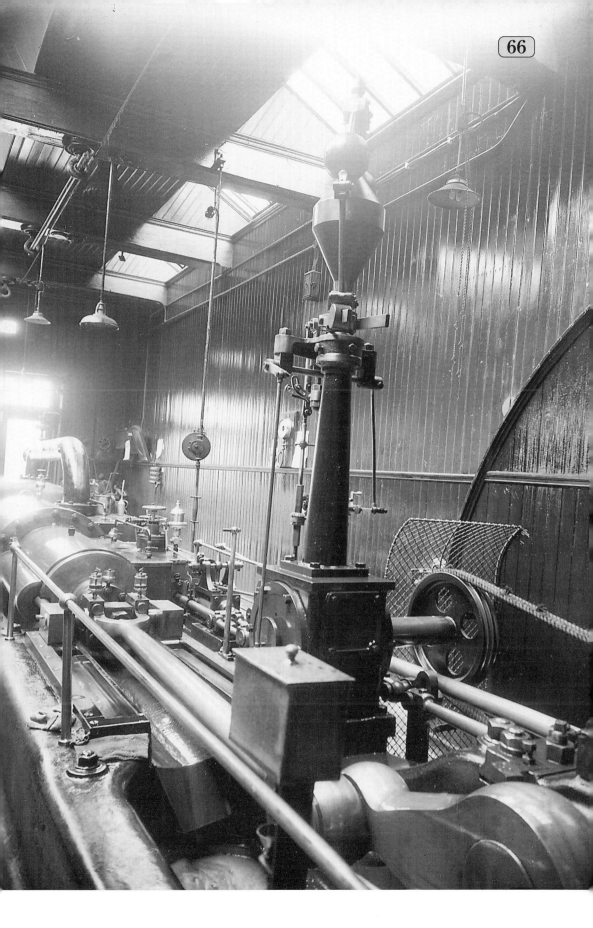

67 Lees Ltd., Dene Mill Triangle, Nr Halifax   SER 59

Type:	Single McNaughted Beam
Photo taken:	1936
Maker and Date:	Wood Bros., Sowerby Bridge? Date unknown
Cylinder/dimensions:	22in x 3ft 6in – Corliss Valves; 30in x 7ft slide valve
Service:	Woollen mill gear drives by vertical shaft?

Beam 21ft 0in long. Flywheel 25ft 0in diameter.

This was an old mill which was acquired by Lees about 1870, when the engine was still a single cylinder. It was McNaughted in the 1890s by Woodhouse and Mitchell, probably when the boiler was worn out. This and the nearby Kebroyd Mill were at one time both owned by Lees, using the same chimney and this continued when Kebroyd was sold to another firm, who were still at work after Lees had ceased. The two mills were about 100 yards apart, with the chimney up on an adjacent hill. This was a frequent practice with the mills in the Yorkshire valleys where to secure adequate chimney draught would have meant very high stacks. Most of the valley mills were scrapped in the 1939-1945 period and probably these were closed but Dene Mill is working and greatly enlarged.

68 Roger Shackleton & Co., Hawksclough Mill, Mytholmroyd SER 60

Type:	Vertical Single Crank	
Photo taken:	1936	
Maker and Date:	Unknown, c1850?	
Cylinder/dimensions:	9in x 3ft 6in and 18in x 3ft 0in – Slide Valves	
Hp: Approx. 80	*Rpm:* 60	*Psi:* 100
Service:	Cotton weaving. Helical tooth gear drive to shed; second motion shaft with 7 loom shafts, bevel driven.	

This was installed as a single cylinder engine, possibly with plain slide bar guides, and was compounded by the addition of a high pressure cylinder beside the original one. This was coupled by a heavy motion beam and parallel motion to the original one, so that the two still drove on to the same crank. No date was known for this alteration but it was probably in the 1890s, again when the old boiler had to be replaced. At the sale in 1957, the engine was bought for scrap for £85. It had no doubt worked for a century, nearly 50 years of which were for Shackletons. The shed contained 720 feet of shafting which was sold for £102, but much more of the machinery went to the firm's Mitchell Hey Mill in Rochdale, which in turn was closed about 1960. There was one Cornish Boiler with a Proctor's mechanical stoker.

69 Joseph Speak & Co., Ing Wood Mills, West Vale, Halifax   SER 617

Type:	Twin Cylinder Vertical – Condensing	
Photo taken:	1953	
Maker and Date:	Maker unknown, 1863	
Cylinder/dimensions:	$8 \frac{1}{4}$ and 16in x 3ft 6in – Corliss and Slide Valves	
Hp: 100	*Rpm:* 60	*Psi:* 120
Service:	Woollen spinning. Disused 1950.	

This was said to have been installed to develop 350 hp as a double cylinder simple expansion engine, driving the original mill. It was greatly altered by Woodhouse and Mitchell in 1922, to use the higher steam pressure of the boilers for the new tandem engine (see SER 108b). A new Corliss valve high pressure cylinder was provided on one side, and the crosshead guiding system was altered on the other side (as shown in the photograph) from the original parallel motion system. The engine was used considerably after this, but was little used in the 1950s. The Mills closed before 1961.

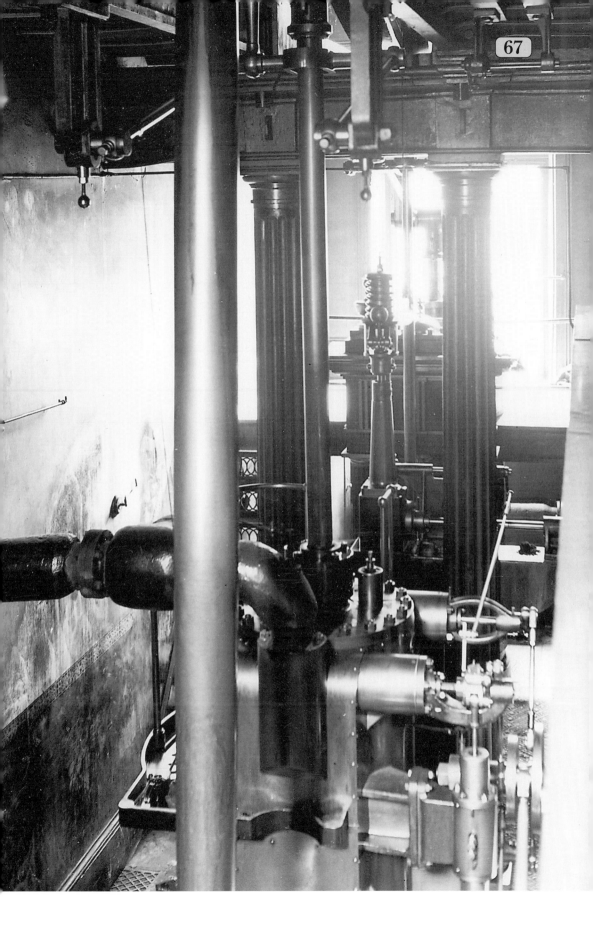

67

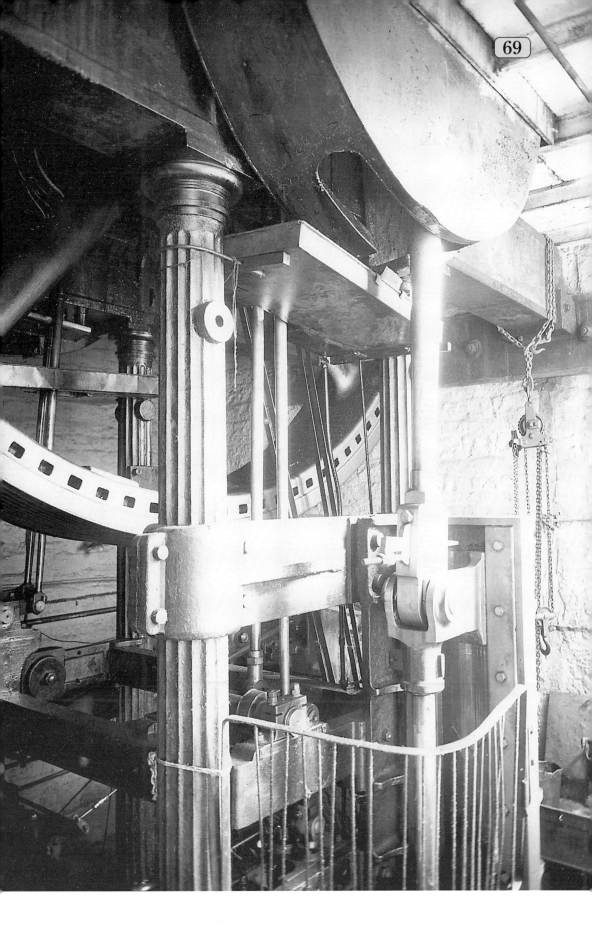

70 Jackson, Feather & Co., Smithfield Mill, Elland, Leeds   SER 619a

Type:	Inverted Vertical – Triple Expansion
Photo taken:	1953
Maker and Date:	Scott and Hodgson, Guide Bridge, Manchester
Cylinder/dimensions:	15; 24in; 39 $^1/_4$in x 3ft 6in – Corliss and Piston Valves
Hp: 750	*Rpm:* 95 *Psi:* 160
Service:	Worsted Spinning.

This was brought from Manchester Docks in a very rusty and neglected state, and was returned to Scott and Hodgsons for overhaul, before installation at Elland in 1925. It gave very good service there, and the mill was electrically driven and working in the early 1970s.

71 Copley Mills, Copley, Nr Halifax   SER 619b

Type:	Horizontal Four Cylinder Triple Expansion
Photo taken:	1953
Maker and Date:	J and E Wood, Bolton, Date unknown
Cylinder/dimensions:	
Hp: 1000	*Rpm:* 75 *Psi:* 160
Service:	Cotton spinning. Rope drive.

This was of interest as a surviving cotton mill in a predominantly woollen area, and also as a Lancashire engine where Yorkshire-made engines were usual. It remained unaltered until the mill was converted to electric drive in the 1950s.

73 Calvert Bros., Illingworth, Nr Halifax   SER 929

Type:	Horizontal Cross Compound
Photo taken:	1958
Maker and Date:	Wood Bros., Sowerby Bridge, 1878
Cylinder/dimensions:	18in and 36in x 4ft 0in – Corliss and Slide Valves
Hp: 300	*Rpm:* 80 *Psi:* 120
Service:	Woollen mills. Belt drives.

This was almost certainly built with piston valves on both cylinders, and the Corliss valve high pressure was fitted by Woodhouse and Mitchell probably in 1892, the date of the Fernihough (of Stalybridge) boiler of 120 p.s.i. which ran the mills for heating and power. It was typical Wood Bros. design, except for the high pressure cylinder and bed, and retained the wooden lagging on the low pressure cylinder. The drives were all by belts from the flywheel rim, which was about 28 inch wide, and were unusual in that there were two, a 20 inch and a 24 inch, running one on top of the other, to drive separate mill shafts. The drives to the floors were by nearly vertical belts, passing to one floor up, where there was another belt to the next floor. The weaving shed was driven by an inclined belt across a roadway. The mills ran thus until they were closed in the mid-1960s, when all including the building was demolished.

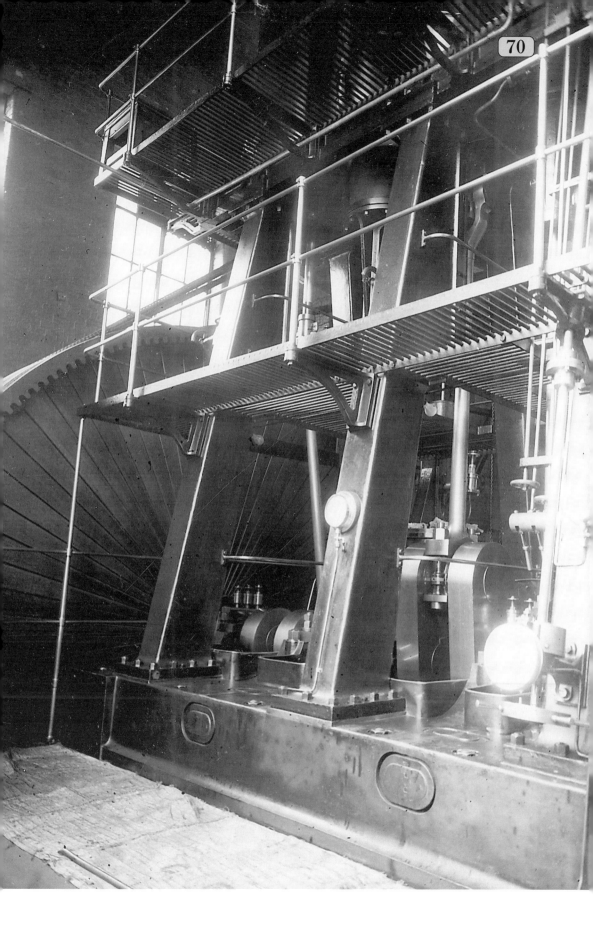

73 Tom Lees & Co., Honley,   SER 1386

Type:	Horizontal Single Cylinder – Condensing
Photo taken:	1969
Maker and Date:	Kilburns, Meltham, 1872
Cylinder/dimensions:	20in x 3ft 0in – Slide Valve
Hp: Approx. 80	Rpm: 70 Psi: 55
Service:	Plant drive by gearing. Dyers to the woollen trade.

The works were established in 1872, and the dyeing vats were direct furnace fired until 1920, when Tom Lees bought the business. He had a great struggle to keep going in the depression of that time, but, first putting in a small boiler, began heating with steam and then managed a larger boiler. It was typical of the Yorkshire attitude that he did not give up, and the works still ran in the 1970s. The engine had been there from the start, and drove by bevel wheels on the crankshaft and a short vertical shaft to the main dyehouse shaft, which crossed above the engine into the dyehouse at the left, to drive the machines by belts. The condenser was under the crosshead guides, with the air pump driven from the crosshead itself. The governor was driven from the main shaft overhead, not the engine crankshaft. The engine remained as it was built except for metallic piston and valve rod packings, and was in use in 1971.

74 John Maude (Clog Soles), Hebden Bridge   SER 1232

Type:	Horizontal Single Tandem
Photo taken:	1966
Maker and Date:	Wood Bros., Valley Foundry, Sowerby Bridge, c.1890
Cylinder/dimensions:	9in and 17 $\frac{1}{2}$in x 2ft 6in – Corliss and Slide Valves
Hp: 100	Rpm: 90 Psi: 100
Service:	Works drive. 14in belt off 10ft flywheel.

This may have been altered by fitting a Corliss valve high pressure cylinder in place of a slide valve originally fitted, but there was no positive history. The massive stone mill was probably built by Maudes, using a water wheel sometime, and a larger engine and boiler were said to have been bought, never installed and then sold. The drives from the mainshaft to the upper and lower floors (the engine was set at road level but there were lower parts at the rear) were all by belts, and there did not appear to have been much alteration in this. There was a single Cornish boiler by Holdsworth of 1891, still used in the 1960s, although all of the drives were by electric motors from 1955. The Corliss valves on the high pressure cylinder were all upon the top suggesting that the Corliss valves were not original. The demand for the healthy clogs died out, and the mill was closed, as was the small country plant (see SER 1277). The plant at the latter was certainly all then sold and removed.

75 Blackburn, Tolson Ltd., Walkley Mill, Heckmondwike   SER 926

Type:	Horizontal Single Tandem
Photo taken:	1958
Maker and Date:	Newton, Bean, Mitchell, Bradford, 1935
Cylinder/dimensions:	15in and 26in x 3ft 0in – Corliss Valves
Hp: 350	Rpm: 80 Psi: 150

This was said to be the last complete mill engine made for a Yorkshire mill, replacing a tandem in another room, very near to this, which was coupled by ropes to the three sections of weaving sheds. Again illustrating how the quality of finish was maintained, the makers in this case carried on a flourishing engine repair business until   the 1960s. The engine was a standard N.B.M. type, which, heavily loaded at times, had never given trouble, and was in perfect condition when, upon the business changing hands in 1963, it was scrapped, since the new owners had different machinery with electric drives. The lagging was very neat, even to the flywheel covering being sheet metal.

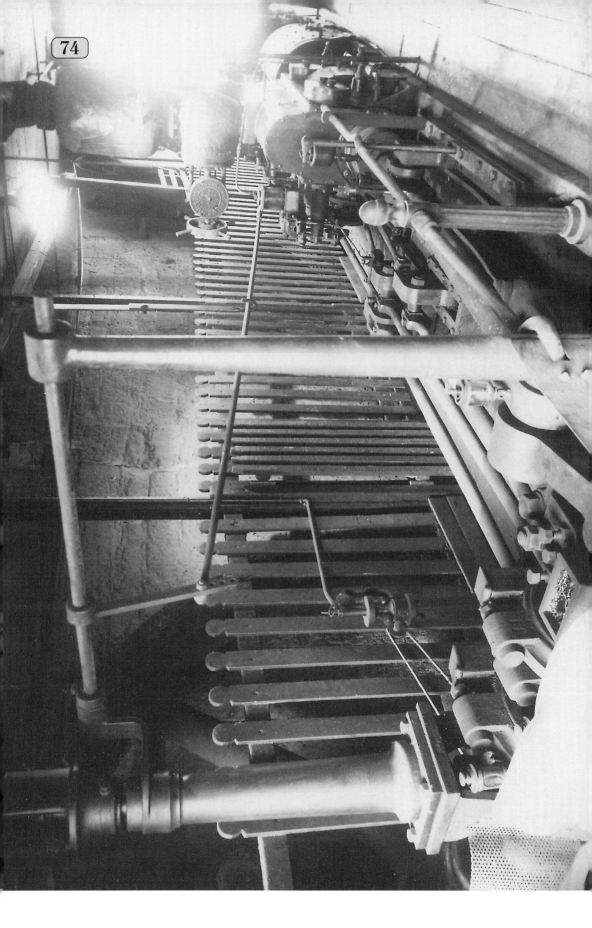

76 Hemsworth Colliery, Nr Hemsworth   SER 1411

Type:	Horizontal Double Cylinder
Photo taken:	1970
Maker and Date:	Probably Markham, 1906-7
Cylinder/dimensions:	40in x 7ft 0in – Cornish Valves
Hp: ?	*Rpm:* 45 *Psi:* 100
Service:	Coal winding. Shaft 689 yards deep. Rope drum 18ft to 30ft

The pit was sunk in about 1878, and was greatly altered in 1906-7, when two Markham winders and new headgears of the same size were installed. To keep the pit running during the change, the new engines were installed at right angles to the original ones, and were rapidly coupled in when ready. They were large engines carrying a coal payload of 4$\frac{1}{2}$ tons per wind, but later a 6 ton skip was used, probably with tail ropes. Electrical winding was installed for the coal drawing shaft in the mid 1960s, and the other steam winder seen in the photograph was to be replaced early in 1970. The colliery was long, a busy one, drawing some 54 winds per hour with the large engines and well equipped shaft and landing arrangements. Automatic steam cut-off gear was fitted, operated by the speed governor. It was to be scrapped when the new winder was installed on this, latterly the men and material shaft.

77 Marshall Flax Mills, Holbeck, Leeds   SER 1020

Type:	Mill Buildings
Photo taken:	1960

Mr Marshall developed the art of flax spinning by great industry to make a sound concern, and the last great additions to the whole were the Egyptian style mill and office buildings all designed on the lines of the office block. The main mill block was driven by a large Hick double beam engine of 1840, with cylinders of 50 inch bore x 5 feet stroke, and the engine and boiler house still remain. The business was closed about 1884 and all of the plant was sold by auction. The buildings are now well cared for by Messr. Kaye & Co., the mail order sales concern, or they may have well been demolished by 1970. Mr Marshall started the business in the late-18th century.

78 Watkinsons, Washpit Mills, Holmfirth   SER 1091

Type:	Horizontal Single Tandem Compound
Photo taken:	1962
Maker and Date:	Pollit & Wigzell, 1909
Cylinder/dimensions:	18in and 34in x 4ft 0in – Corliss Valves
Hp: 600	*Rpm:* 80 *Psi:* 160
Service:	Woollen manufacture. Drive partly by ropes, also to alternator, 250 KVA.

A typical Pollit & Wigzell engine, this had one unusual feature, that the engine bed was deeper than usual at the low pressure end, where there were deep loops cast in for access to the low pressure exhaust valves. The whole bed was certainly deep and stiff, and other than fitting a Lumb governor, little had been changed, or much repair needed despite a fully loaded life. An uncommon feature was the fitting of an oil separator in the exhaust steam pipe, which, in extracting most of the oil from the exhaust allowed the warm water to be used for wool washing. The mill was run with high economy, and much of the heat in the exhaust steam was recovered from the condenser water. The use of soft packing on the low pressure piston rod glands was unusual. The engine continued in full use in 1975. There was also a back pressure turbine and generator in use.

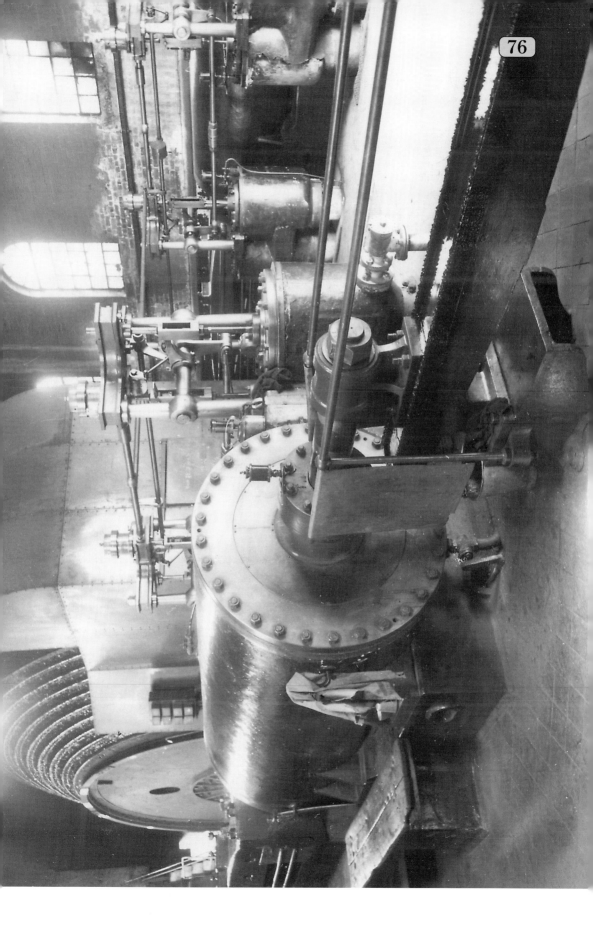

79 Wright, Hinchcliffe & Co., Valley Dye Works, Holmfirth   SER 1350

Type:	Horizontal Single Cylinder – Non-Condensing
Photo taken:	1968
Maker and Date:	Calvert & Co., Huddersfield, c.1880s?
Cylinder/dimensions:	12in x 2ft 0in – Slide Valve
Hp: 20	*Rpm:* 90 *Psi:* 90
Service:	Plant drive. 9in belt off pulley.

The small dyehouse had the usual roller type machines for working the dye thoroughly into the fabrics. Each machine took a heavy load at starting, but the intermittent operation allowed the small engine to run about a dozen, all belt driven from the single overhead main driving shaft. The little plant was closed about 1971 and regrettably when the plant was scrapped the little engine, probably the last of Calvert's to survive, was destroyed for the brass parts.

80 Robinson, Smithy Place Mills, Brockholes, Nr Holmfirth   SER 276

Type:	McNaughted Single Beam
Photo taken:	1939
Maker and Date:	Unknown
Cylinder/dimensions:	Slide Valves
Hp:	*Rpm:* *Psi:*
Service:	Gear drive converted to ropes.

Nothing was known of the history of this engine, but it was known to have run away on several occasions (each time without a smash) possibly due to governor trouble. There was nothing in the design that would suggest the maker, but the McNaughting and no doubt the conversion to rope drives was by Schofield & Taylor. The old gear drives were said to be audible half a mile away. The engine was scrapped in c.1962.

81 H & S Butterworth, Lower Mills, Holmfirth   SER 278

Type:	McNaught & Pusher Compounded Beam
Photo taken:	1939
Maker and Date:	Unknown, c1840s
Cylinder/dimensions:	21in x 4ft 0in and 17 $\frac{1}{2}$in x 2ft 0in – Slide Valve
	15in x 3ft 0in – Corliss Valves
Hp: 270	*Rpm:* 65 *Psi:* 120
Service:	Woollen manufacturers. Weaving shed.
	Beam 12ft 6in long; flywheel 13ft 0in diameter.

This was undoubtedly the most heavily loaded engine in the trade. When built it ran at 45 rpm, probably using steam at 20 psi. More power was needed about 1870 and a new cylinder and boiler for 50 psi were fitted. More power still was required by 1894, when it was McNaughted by Schofield & Taylor, and a boiler for 90 psi installed. By 1915 this too was insufficient, so a horizontal Corliss valve and pusher was installed, with a boiler for 120 psi. This was all that was safe structurally, so to get more power, it was later speeded up to 65 rpm, when no insurance company would accept the risk. Yet is is a fact that this small engine never failed and was still working when electric drives were installed about 1959. There was also a separate shed engine which was little used.

82 Barber & Co., Holmbridge, Nr Holmfirth   SER 879

Type:	Uniflow Single
Photo taken:	1957
Maker and Date:	Clayton and Goodfellows, Blackburn, 1922
Cylinder/dimensions:	24in x 2ft 6in
Hp: 520	*Rpm:* 150 *Psi:* 150
Service:	Woollen weaving. Electricity generating.

This was supplied new to Bannermans, Bee Mill, Ribchester, near Preston, in 1922 and was removed to Barber's mill some 30 years later by Richard Inman of Huddersfield. It was believed to have retained the original rope driving pulley for the generator drive at Barbers. At the other side of the road to the mill, it drove by motors as did the Pollit & Wigzell engine it replaced in 1951. Originally there was a beam engine driving the shed directly by gearing, but this was replaced by the electric drives, due to lack of room for the larger engine near to the shed. The uniflow engine was in regular use in 1971.

83 Gledhill Bros., Bridge Mills, Holmfirth   SER 880

Type:	Inverted Vertical Compound
Photo taken:	1957
Maker and Date:	Wood Bros., Sowerby Bridge, 1913
Cylinder/dimensions:	17 $\frac{1}{2}$in and 33in x 3ft 0in – Corliss Valves
Hp: 450	*Rpm:* 91 *Psi:* 140
Service:	Woollen mill drive.

The mills were originally driven by a single cylinder beam engine with gear drives. The other mill across the road was driven by a shaft in a tunnel beneath the road, to the vertical shaft which was in the middle of the mill. The beam engine was assisted by a Schofield and Taylor horizontal single cylinder pusher engine exhausting to the beam engine. More power was needed in 1938, and this engine, from another mill, was then installed in a house at the end of the mill, driving by ropes back to the original second motion shaft and gearing. It gave every satisfaction, and ran until about 1962, when the flywheel failed as the engine was being started one morning. The mill was then turned over to motor drives, mainly with a motor to each floor.

84 Jarrett, Pyrah and Armitage, Quay Street, Huddersfield   SER 1349

Type:	Horizontal Single Tandem – Condensing
Photo taken:	1968
Maker and Date:	Wood, Baldwin?, 1880s?
Cylinder/dimensions:	11in and 18 $\frac{1}{2}$in x 3ft 0in – Corliss and Slide Valves.
Hp: 150	*Rpm:* 104 *Psi:* 100
Service:	Works drive. Was to shafting, later to alternator.

 Sawmilling has been carried on here since 1770, and a beam engine was installed to drive the early machinery by gears and underground, as well as overhead shafting, using spur and bevel wheels. The present engine was installed in 1906, to drive the same shafting by ropes, but most of the overhead shafts were then abandoned. In 1958, with extensive rearranging with machines with built-in motors, the change to electrical drive throughout was necessary, and an 115 kW alternator was installed to assist the Grid load. The engine continued working 1973.

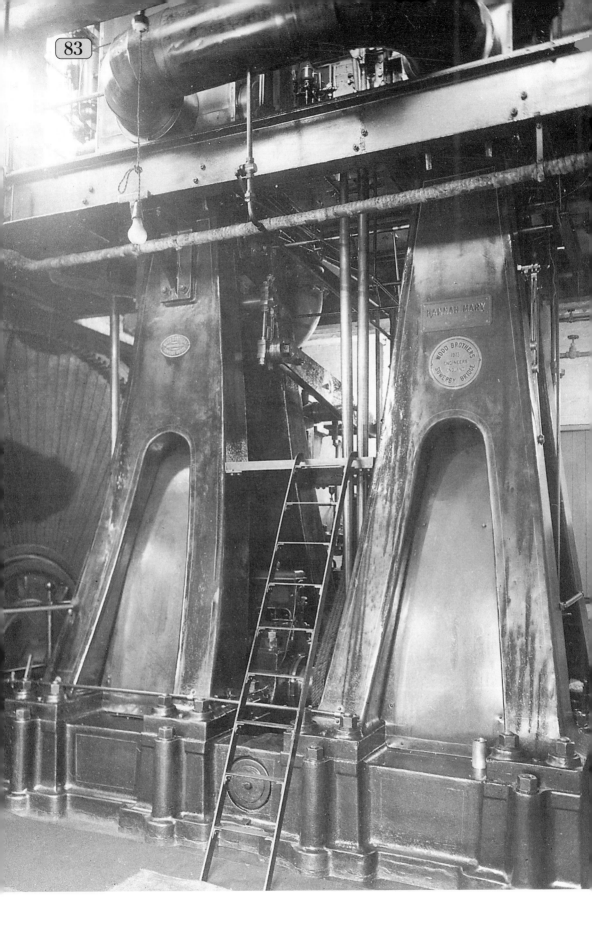

85 The Fieldhouse Engine, The Tolson Museum, Huddersfield   SER 1402

Type:	Horizontal Return Connecting Rod
Photo taken:	1970
Maker and Date:	Maker unknown, c.1850?
Cylinder/dimensions:	9in x 2ft 0in – Slide Valve
Hp: Approx. 20	*Rpm:* 40 *Psi:* 50
Service:	Open air exhibit.

The fireclay pit from which this hauled the clay was probably started on the site of an old colliery about 1850, to work the fireclay bands in the mine, but it is doubtful if it was the colliery engine. It was certainly altered later to drive on the opposite hand, possibly when it was rearranged to haul railway trucks up from the works yard, as against hauling the clay up from the pit which it had earlier done. It was fully over-hauled (after the owners, The Leeds Fireclay Co. had kindly presented it for preservation) by Messrs. Broadbent of Huddersfield, and now, well protected from the weather by the roof can be readily seen in the open air beside the museum and park just outside Huddersfield.

86 J B Brierley & Co., Turnbridge, Huddersfield   SER 273

Type:	Two McNaughted Beam
Photo taken:	1939
Maker and Date:	R & J Gledhill, Bradley Mill, Huddersfield, 1872
Cylinder/dimensions:	48in x 7ft 0in – Slide Valve and 30in x 3ft 6in – Corliss Valve
Hp: 460	*Rpm:* 24 *Psi:* 100?
Service:	Woollen mill. Gear drives to vertical shafts.

There were two mills each with a similar engine, probably by the same maker and each driving its own mill. The earlier was said to date from 1846, and the later could have been earlier than 1872, as the cast iron eccentric rod was of an old design. Both were McNaughted by Schofield & Taylor about 1904. The older one was fitted with a new slide valve, flywheel and crank in 1896. Each of the engines had been heavily loaded, so that weakness developed in the beam centre bearings, and both engines had struts taken from the bearing caps to the girders of the floor above.

87 Sellers, Leemills, Scholes, Nr Huddersfield   SER 277

Type:	Single McNaughted Beam
Photo taken:	1939
Maker and Date:	Unknown
Cylinder/dimensions:	23in x 2ft 3in and 26in x 5ft 0in – Slide Valves
Hp: 160	*Rpm:* 57 *Psi:* 100
Service:	Woollen mill. Drive by electric motors.

This was extremely well kept, and with the vee-belt drives to the alternator, was very quiet. It was McNaughted in 1886, and a new LP cylinder was fitted in 1896, but nothing else was known of it, but it was probably of local make. Due to overloading, the entablature had been strutted down by stays from the upper floor, in the same way as other engines in the area had. It was a practice not met elsewhere. Its end was not known.

88 Wells & Co., Phoenix Mill, Huddersfield   SER 337

Type:	Single Cylinder Beam
Photo taken:	1947
Maker and Date:	Bowling Ironworks Co., 1845-50
Cylinder/dimensions:	34in x 7ft 0in – Slide Valves
Hp: Approx. 200	*Rpm:* 20 *Psi:* 80
Service:	Woollen spinning. Gear drives, two vertical shafts, one in each of two mill blocks. Beam 20ft centres Flywhell 25ft diameter.

The mills were built between 1845 & 50, and there had been no alteration in the engine, which worked for over 90 years, but the greatly increased loads of later years had led to many motor driven units. Even so, the engine carried most of the load until the mill was closed about 1945. There were two boilers some distance from the engine but one was condemned and the other was only allowed 50 psi. The engine ran very well, certainly without losing mill time, in the last 5 years of work.

89 Naylor Bros. Denby Dale, Nr Huddersfield   SER 924

Type:	Horizontal Single Tandem
Photo taken:	1958
Maker and Date:	Burnley Ironworks, 1914
Cylinder/dimensions:	15in and 30in x 3ft 6in – Corliss Valves
Hp: 350	*Rpm:* 80 *Psi:* 120
Service:	Earthenware manufacture.

This was purchased from a weaving shed in Burnley, which was closed in 1936. Burnley Ironworks did not build many tandems, and this may have been in Slaters in Calder Valley, Burnley, who did have a Burnley Ironworks tandem. It ran very well until the works were turned over to electric driving in 1958 and the engine scrapped. Despite the dust around a clay grinding plant, the engine was very well kept by a good engineer. It drove by 8 or 10 ropes to the mill shaft, probably retaining the original flywheel. This also had the condenser tandem on the rear of the low pressure cylinder.

90 Hull Waterworks, Springhead Station   SER 115

Type:	Cornish Beam
Photo taken:	1935
Maker and Date:	Bells, Lightfoot & Co., Newcastle on Tyne, 1876
Cylinder/dimensions:	90in x 11ft 0in – Equal Beam
Service:	Town supply. Well to reservoir. 2–27in bucket well and 1-36in ram pumps, forcing to reservoir. Beam 40ft 0in long x 8ft 0in deep.

Very attractive Cornish type engine, with massive beam built entirely of iron plates and angle iron and rivetted throughout. The circular staircase to give access to the upper parts of the engine is very unusual in this type, so too is the provision for a variable load upon the surface force pump. The usual Cornish style is a massive cast iron weight upon the surface pump plunger, but here it is a water tank, 9ft in diameter, with a variable water weight. A delivery pipe from an overhead tank was fixed to deliver water to the tank, but did not move with the tank, i.e. it slid in the hole on the top, with a drain valve at the bottom of the tank by which it could be partly drained to reduce the total weight, and so the head against it.

89

91 Chambers & Fargus Ltd., High Flaggs Oil Mill, Hull   SER 150

Type:	Woolf Compound Beam
Photo taken:	1936
Maker and Date:	King & Menzies – date unknown
Cylinder/dimensions:	12in x 3ft 6in Slide, altered to 18in x 5ft 0in Piston Valves
Hp:	*Rpm:* *Psi:*
Service:	Direct to mill shaft, not geared.
	Beam 16ft 0in long. Flywheel 18ft 0in diameter.

This was a lightly made engine whose general design suggested 1840-50 date. It was built as a compound, with a single side valve for the two cylinders, replaced by a piston valve for each but retaining the old lattice eccentric rod. The engine was replaced by an expeller mill in 1948.

92 Chambers & Fargus Ltd, High Flaggs Oil Mill, Hull   SER 379a

Type:	Woolf Compound Beam Engine
Photo taken:	1951
Maker and Date:	Thompson & Stather, Hull, c.1870
Cylinder/dimensions:	20in x 3ft 6in and 28in x 5ft 0in – Slide Valves
Hp: Approx. 120	*Rpm:* 25 *Psi:* 50
Service:	Seed crushing and oil mill drive.

Geared drive to overhead mill shaft similar to SER 147, driving seed crushers and press pumps for oil extraction presses. In use until the 1950s, this was a typical heavy oil mill plant. It is probable that Good & Menzies rebuilt the engine, or possibly altered it to compound. Certainly they had done work on it, although Thompson & Stather almost certainly made it. The mills probably closed when oil seed was in short supply in the 1950s

93 Chambers & Fargus Ltd, High Flaggs Oil Mill, Hull   SER 379b

Type:	Willans-Siemens Generating Set – Non-Condensing
	Willans Engine, No. 662 – sizes unknown
	Siemens Generator, No. 2469a
Photo taken:	1951
Maker and Date:	
Cylinder/dimensions:	
Hp: 10kw	*Rpm:* 450 *Psi:* 50
Service:	Electric lighting.

Typical small set of the early electric lighting period before widespread public supply became available. This was little used after 1935, but was possibly preserved after the mills closed in the 1950s.

94 The West Dock Sewage Pumping Station, Hull   SER 888

Type:	Three Inverted Vertical Cross Compound – Condensing
Photo taken:	1957
Maker and Date:	James Watt & Co., 1883
Cylinder/dimensions:	18in and 30in x 4ft 0in – Piston Valves
Hp:.Approx.150 each	*Rpm:* 18 *Psi:* 100
Service:	Town sewage pumps. Bucket pumps under engine.

These were plain compact engines with a bucket pump below each cylinder, driven from the crossheads, and with the connecting rods driving up to the crankshaft. Each was named after a councillor, i.e. Hollitt, Willows, and Massey. The high pressure valve was of the Rookes internal cut-off type, with hand variation of the admission. The general design was plain but sound, as very little other than running repairs had been needed until they were scrapped when diesel electric plant was installed in 1957-8. Hull is entirely dependent upon pumping to avoid sewer flooding, owing to the flatness of the area. The clean conditions were typical of a responsible authority's attention.

95 The Co-operative Society, The Flour Mill, Hull   SER 990

Type:	Horizontal Cross Compound – Condensing
Photo taken:	1959
Maker and Date:	W & J Yates, Blackburn? , c.1890
Cylinder/dimensions:	23in and 45in x 4ft 6in – (Musgraves) drop piston valves
Hp: 1200	*Rpm:* 85 *Psi:* 180
Service:	Mill drive by 22 ropes to floor and alternator.

The history was not positive, but this may have had slide valves until the Musgrave's cylinders were installed in 1915. Musgrave's records state that it was a conversion from a three cylinder triple expansion to a cross compound. The mill was converted to electric driving in 1959-60. The condenser air pump drive, behind the cylinders in Musgrave's designs, was later changed to an Edwards three-throw type with rope drive. The three boilers by Hewitt and Kellett were installed in 1927, with superheaters. It was lightly built for its power, yet gave little trouble, and often ran 5 or more weeks non-stop. It was scrapped on the change to electric driving. The mill had belonged to Hurtley's previously.

96 Gill, Stansfield & Co., Cowling, Nr Keighley   SER 1023

Type:	Locomobile Overtype Compound – Condensing
Photo taken:	1960
Maker and Date:	Garrett & Co., Leiston, No. 33872, 1921
Cylinder/dimensions:	Approx. 19in and 16in x 1ft 9in – Piston Valves
Hp: 250	*Rpm:* 160 *Psi:* 190
Service:	Cotton weaving, 9 rope drive to two weaving sheds.

The concern was established in the mid-19th century as far as could be traced, and was driven by a beam engine until the Garrett was installed. It was highly economical, using less than half of the fuel that the beam engine did. The yarn was bought from outside sizers, but in 1925 Stansfields decided to size the yarn themselves, and the boiler was insufficient for this. A Lancashire boiler for 190 p.s.i. made by Hewett and Kellet, Bradford, was installed, and with this, ample steam was available for the engine and the processing, until it was decided to adopt electric driving in 1961 when the engine was scrapped, although the boiler was retained.

96

97 J & J Craven Ltd. Dalton Mills, Keighley   SER 1066a

Type:	Two Horizontal Tandem Compound
Photo taken:	1961
Maker and Date:	Pollit & Wigzell, 1904
Cylinder/dimensions:	22in and 42in x 5ft – Corliss Valves
Hp: 1000	*Rpm:* 65 *Psi:* 130
Service:	Woollen mills. Room and power for small groups as well.

Dalton mills were built in the 1860s, and fitted with the largest beam engine in a textile mill. This drove by two shafts and pinions from a gear ring on the flywheel arms, a shaft going under the mill yard to one block. A shaft broke and the pinion rolled under the gear drive wheel in 1904. So severely damaged was the engine that it was decided to replace it and the drives, by two engines as above. There 12 Cornish boilers originally, which were replaced by six supplying higher pressure for the Pollit engines, which served until the drives were all converted to electric motors by 1966. The engines were named *Zilda* which was stopped about 1964, and *Jennie* which was finally stopped in 1966; the end of engines at Dalton after just under a century. The mill was highly ornate and very costly as was the chimney, which originally had a tapering top part, and cast iron grill work. It was said that the beam engine and gearing cost nearly £12,000 in the 1860s, and the power installation took nearly seven years to complete.

98 J & J Craven Ltd. Dalton Mills, Keighley   SER 1066b

Type:	Millgearing Frames
Photo taken:	1961
Maker and Date:	Wm. Bracewell & Co., Burnley, 1860s
Service:	Upper floor drive of No. 9 mill.

The millgearing at Dalton was in keeping with the rest. Each floor had a single mainshaft which was originally driven from a vertical shaft driven by bevel wheels from the shaft under the mill yard to No 9 mill. The Pollit engine was arranged to drive the two floors by ropes from the flywheel. The photograph shows supporting columns for the mainshaft of the upper floor which started at 8 inches in diameter and was reduced to 6 inches for most of the length of some 200 ft. The machinery on the upper floor were driven from cross shafts which were driven by bevel wheels from the central main shaft. The shaft can be seen overhead in the photograph and one of the bevel wheel casings can also be seen beyond the first column. This framing was a part of the mill structure and had to be retained although the shafting was probably taken out when electrical drives were installed.

99 Peter Green & Co., Bradley, Nr Keighley   SER 1105

Type:	Horizontal Single Tandem
Photo taken:	1962
Maker and Date:	Smith Bros. and Eastwood, Bradford, 1901
Cylinder/dimensions:	14in and 28in x 3ft 6in – Corliss Valves
Hp: 300	*Rpm:* 80 *Psi:* 140
Service:	Woollen mill. Driven by 8 ropes from 13ft 6in flywheel.

The makers probably only produced two or three engines but this one was very good, and certainly ran for over 70 years, with very little repair. The valve gear, Eastwood's patent, was very similar to the later Musgrave's type, with broad massive dies. It was named   and re-placed a beam engine which was originally in the present rope race. The new engine was placed in the space needed for one of the two boilers which the beam engine required, and this gave good length for a neat rope drive to the mill mainshaft. The rounded crank web resembles the Pollit design. The open flywheel arms are unusual. It was working in 1973.

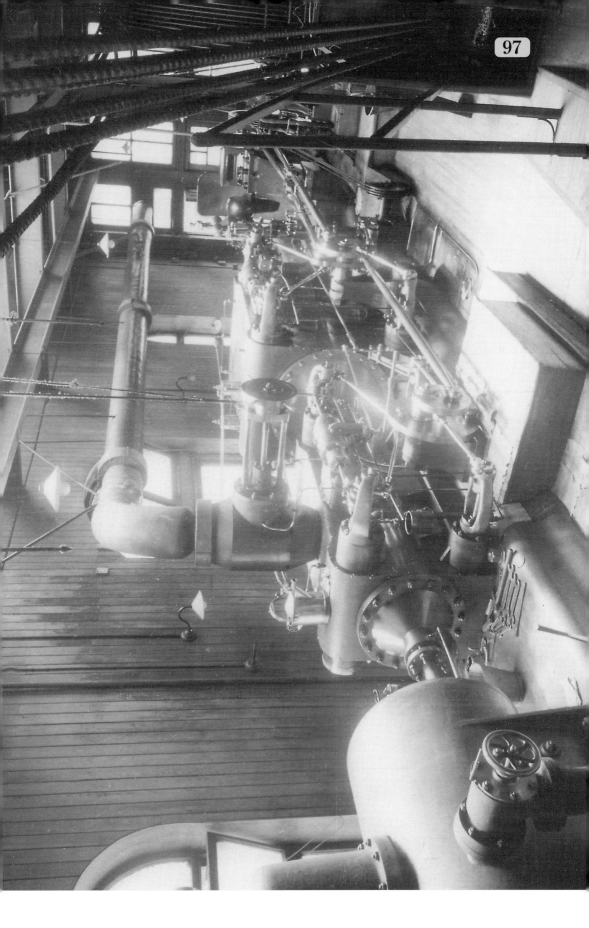

100 Dixon & Co., Bobbin Makers, Steeton, Nr Keighley   SER 1188

Type:	Horizontal Single Tandem Compound
Photo taken:	1965
Maker and Date:	Unknown. Rebuilt by Pollit & Wigzell, 1921
Cylinder/dimensions:	18in and 32in x 4ft 0in – Corliss and Slide Valves
Hp: 450	*Rpm:* 62 *Psi:* 120
Service:	Mill drive by 27in, belt to mainshaft.

This was virtually a new engine built by Pollit's to use the original crankshaft and fly wheel which was all that remained of the original engine. The flywheel arms were of "H" section, similar to those of the Scottish engine builders, but nothing was known of its history. The rebuild was typical Pollit & Wigzell work which ran the plant virtually without repairs until it was closed in 1971-2. The belt drives were interesting in that the mill was driven off the 27 inch inclined belt, with a vertical belt to the electrical genera- tor shaft, both off the 60 inch wide flywheel, but also with a cross coupling belt from the mill shaft to the generator shaft was well.

101 Wilson's Silk Mill, Lothersdale, Nr Keighley   SER 164

Type:	High Breast Water Wheel
Photo taken:	1935
Maker and Date:	Unknown
Cylinder/dimensions:	44ft 0in diameter, 5ft 0 in wide
Hp: Approx. 100	*Rpm:* 50ft head of water? *Psi:*
Service:	Silk mill.

Cast iron rim sections with sheet iron buckets, supported by 18 radial wooden arms on each side, with 18 sets of diagonal iron stays, $1^1/_2$ inch diameter. No indication of the maker. These features were original since the hub and rim sections were designed to accommodate them. The gear drive ring tooth segments bedded upon timber $1^1/_2$ inch thick, are 43ft in diameter, driving into a 5 ft pinion, and thence to the mill shaft by a gear of 10ft diameter, total ratio about 25 to 1. Until electrification the wheel was coupled to a beam engine, later itself assisted by a horizontal engine believed to be connected pusher compound style. These were removed on electrification. The sole plates of the buckets were wooden and non-ventilated.

102 Illingworth & Ingham Ltd, The City Sawmills, Leeds   SER 1080

Type:	Horizontal Single Tandem – Non-Condensing
Photo taken:	1962
Maker and Date:	G Blamires, Cleckheaton, 1890s?
Cylinder/dimensions:	16in and 27in x 4ft 0in – Slide Valves
Hp: 150	*Rpm:* 90 *Psi:* 120
Service:	Sawmill drive, 16in belt drive to shaft under the mill.

This was extremely well kept and ran the sawmills regularly for well over 60 years, when electric motors were installed and the engine was scrapped. It ran economically, using waste timber and some coal as fuel from a single boiler. It was an interesting design with the cylinders independent of the bed, and held only at the ends with 4 stay rods between the main frame and the rear high pressure cylinder. It was scrapped when motors were installed An interesting point was that the governer was away from the engine and at low level on one main steam pipe.

103 *Joshua Wilson & Co., Gotts Mill, Leeds*   SER 1112a

Type:	Horizontal Single Tandem
Photo taken:	1962
Maker and Date:	Woodhouse and Mitchell, Brighouse, 1888
Cylinder/dimensions:	17$^1/_2$in and 30in x 5ft 0in – Corliss Valves
Hp: 500	*Rpm:* 62 *Psi:* 120
Service:	Woollen spinning and weaving 12 rope drive to shed and mill.

The engines at Wilsons were all by Woodhouse, and this one was unusual for the makers in having the valves below the cylinder, the only such design by them I met. It certainly was a good engine and had given little trouble in 75 years at work. The mills were an historic site, having one of the earliest Boulton and Watt Engines in the town, which originally drove several mill buildings by a large central gearwheel under the mill yard, with bevel wheels to several shafts to the buildings. It was still a good business when the local authority compelled closure to provide car parking space in the 1960s.

104 *Joshua Wilson & Co., Gotts Mill, Leeds*   SER 1112b

Type:	Inverted Vertical Compound – Non-Condensing
Photo taken:	1962
Maker and Date:	Woodhouse and Mitchell, 1897
Cylinder/dimensions:	Approx. 9in and 16in x 1ft 6in – Piston Valves
Hp: Approx. 100	*Rpm:* 90 *Psi:* 120
Service:	Electric lighting plant. 6 rope drive.

Wilsons were very early users of electrical lighting and the current was provided by this plant, at first with an Edmistons, (of Kirkstall Rd, Leeds), dynamo driven by the ropes at the left, through the countershaft. Latterly, the generator seen in front of the engine was installed as standby to the Grid current which was later used as the lighting load grew and public supply was available. As with SER 1112a this engine was unusual for Woodhouse and Mitchell as they made very few piston valves, or inverted vertical engines for any purpose. The speed on this engine was controlled by the governor operating an internal piston valve on the high pressure cylinder. The engine had done a lot of work, but remained unaltered. The other two Woodhouse engines at Gotts, were more usual, a tandem mill engine with Corliss HP, and slide low pressure valves, and a small tandem donkey engine with slide valves for part time evening shift work at a small section.

105 *Messrs Knowles & Co., Pipe Works, Elland*   SER 1129

Type:	Horizontal Single Tandem – Non-Condensing
Photo taken:	1963
Maker and Date:	Hick, Hargreaves, Bolton, 1883, as built
Cylinder/dimensions:	15in and 30in x 4ft 0in – Corliss Valve
Hp: 350	*Rpm:* 80 *Psi:* 160
Service:	Drives clay mills and clay preparation plant.

This was the last of the six single cylinder engines suppled for Holden's large combing shed in 1883. Each was 30 inch x 4ft0in stroke, driving a single line shaft from each engine by ropes from the 18 ft flywheel. Hicks supplied numerous large single cylinder mill engines about that time, and several including these six, and the 40in x 10ft 0in single for Whetley mills, were tandem compounded in the early 1920s if not before. This was the last of Holden's six engines to survive, and it lay at Knowles' site for some years before re-erection. Set to work about 1963, it runs a part of the plant at Elland, exhausting to the drying kilns, but has been badly neglected by the men, and was reputed to be in poor condition in 1972. The valve gear was altered when compounded, to the later crab claw type. The original was almost certainly the Spencer Inglis form.

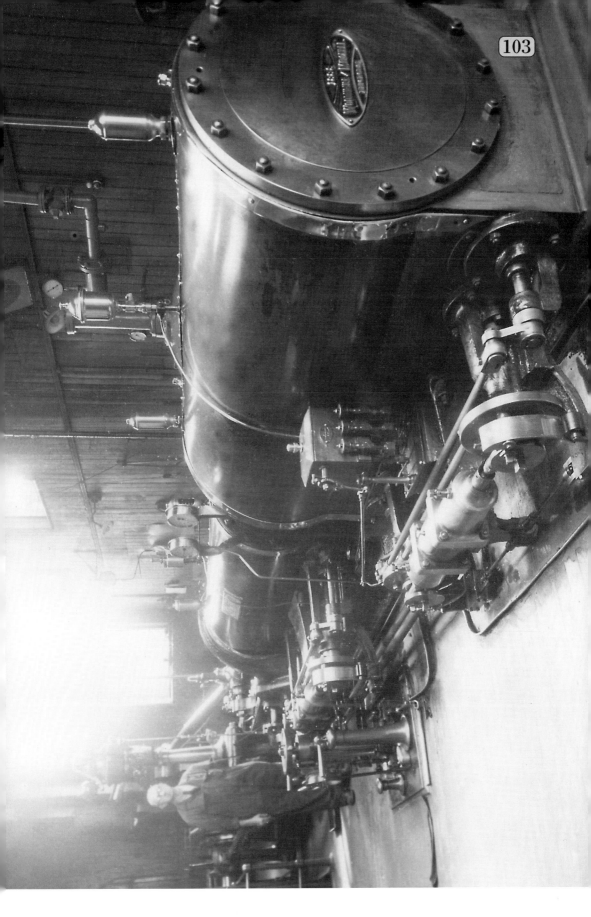

106 Clarke & Co., Textile Dyers, Kirkstall Road, Leeds   SER 1235

Type:	Horizontal Single Cylinder – Non-Condensing
Photo taken:	1966
Maker and Date:	Newton, Bean and Mitchell, c.1900?
Cylinder/dimensions:	12in x 2ft 0in – Corliss Valves
Hp: 100	*Rpm:* 120 *Psi:* 100
Service:	Mill drive, 6 ropes off 7 ft pulley.

This was one of the fastest Corliss valve engines running in later years, i.e. 120 r.p.m. whereas few ran over 90 r.p.m. with trip gear in use. This was certainly very effective and with an unusually heavy flywheel, coped well with the heavy loads, as well as supplying heat to the process system from the exhaust steam. It was secondhand when installed there in 1914, following a overhaul by the makers. It gave well over 50 years of service before the plant was closed in re-development schemes and all scrapped.

107 Water Haigh Colliery, Woodlesford, Nr Leeds   SER 1343

Type:	Horizontal Double Cylinder
Photo taken:	1968
Maker and Date:	Glenfield & Kennedy?, 1912
Cylinder/dimensions:	30in x 5ft 0in – Piston Valves
Hp: ?	*Rpm:* 50 *Psi:* 120
Service:	Coal winding. Upcast No 3 shaft 355 yards deep. Rope drum 16ft diameter.

Glenfield and Kennedy were largely waterworks engineers, once building many steam pumping engines of all types, and latterly made valves and pipe line fittings. This engine was a typical Andrew Barclay, Kilmarnock design, although the counter balanced crank was unusual in their practice. It was said on the site to have been made to Barclay's design by Glenfields, who had certainly made pumping engines to others' designs, as at Addington, Surrey. The Barclay's type drop cut-off valves driven from the piston valve tail rods were probably added later, possibly when new boilers for higher pressure were installed. It was one of the Henry Briggs Co.'s pits, and highly developed by them, with 4 mixed pressure turbines driving alternators and air compressors of some 6-7,000 h.p., and a Robey's cross-compound fan engine (of 180 h.p. and dated 1904), giving 175,000 cubic feet of air per minute. The colliery was latterly a training unit for younger men entering the industry but it was closed and the equipment scrapped in 1972. The No. 1 shaft engine was a Davy Bros. of 1876 moved from Whitwood colliery when it was closed (coal was worked out) in 1912, and it was modified for use at Haigh pit.

108 Hardcastle & Co., Dyers and Finishers, Wortley Road, Leeds   SER 1346

Type:	Horizontal Single Tandem – Condensing
Photo taken:	1968
Maker and Date:	Wood, Baldwin, Brighouse, 1870s?
Cylinder/dimensions:	10$\frac{1}{2}$in and 20in x 3ft 0in – Corliss and Slide Valves
Hp:. 100	Rpm: 85 Psi: 120
Service:	Works drive.

The works were started in 1874, the date on the chimney, probably with a single cylinder engine made by Wood Baldwin's, and the Corliss high pressure was added later possibly around 1911, the date of the earlier boiler. There were two works sections arranged in a line of buildings some 200 feet long, with a single mainshaft along it to drive 22 roller type dyeing machines, and other plant. The cylinders were placed close together with a simple block gland between them in the rear low pressure cover, with the high pressure connected directly behind it. The premises were taken by a chemical concern after Hardcastles closed in 1967.

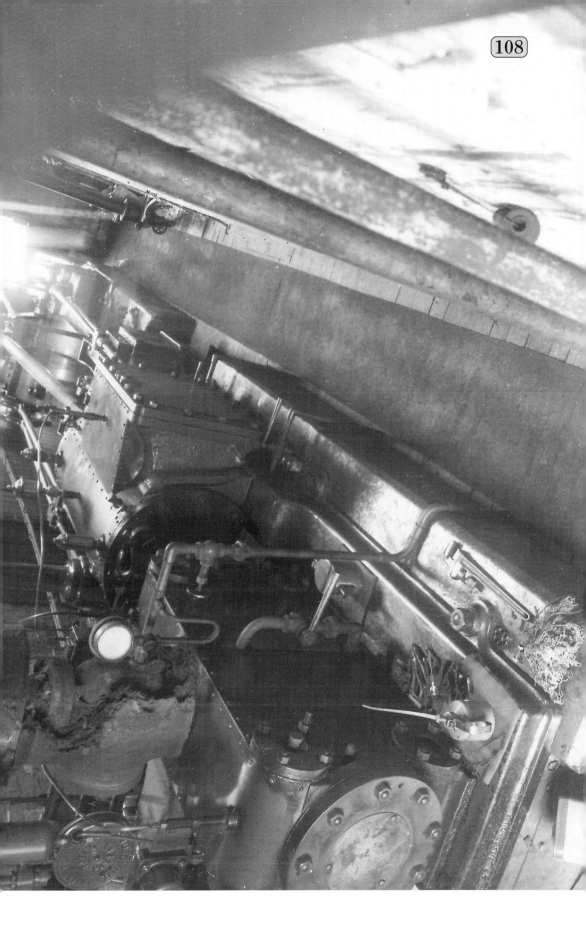

109 Hodgson & Co., Craven Mills, Bramley, Leeds   SER 1387

Type:	Horizontal Single Tandem – Condensing
Photo taken:	1969
Maker and Date:	Cole, Marchent and Morley, Bradford, 1914
Cylinder/dimensions:	15 $^1/_2$in and 30in x 3ft 6in – Drop, Piston Valves
Hp: 450	*Rpm:* 96 *Psi:* 160
Service:	Works drive by 12 ropes of 16 ft flywheel.

The engine was supplied new when the fine stone mill was built in 1913-14, and ran it until it was closed in 1972, when with the premises in a different business, the engine was not needed. It was Cole Marchent's standard design which, met everywhere, was noted for reliability, trouble free running and with superheat, the high economy attained. Certainly very little had ever needed to be done to it in 55 years at work, (and its condition was perfect still). Away from any cooling water source, and closely built around, a cooling tower was installed at the start, and always provided the cooling water for the condenser.

110 F A Lodge & Co., Stonebridge Mill, Leeds   SER 1491a

Type:	Vertical Steam Engine and Pumps
Photo taken:	1975
Maker and Date:	Both unknown
Cylinder/dimensions:	10 $^1/_2$in x 1ft 6in
Hp: Approx. 10	*Rpm:* 60 (engine) *Psi:* 50
Service:	Mill water service.

This comprised twin ram pumps driven by gearing from a combined engine. Although disused, it was very well made, dating probably from about 1870-80. The pumps were 5in diameter rams by 1ft 6ins stroke, and supplied the works from a reservoir, filling a tank on the roof. The site contains some of the oldest works in Yorkshire, with a unique children's school and laboratory of very early 19th century date. It was hoped to save the latter.

111 F A Lodge & Co., Stonebridge Mill, Leeds   SER 1491b

Type:	Hydraulic Pressure Pump and Engine
Photo taken:	1975
Maker and Date:	Date unknown – Edwin Mills & Son, Huddersfield
Cylinder/dimensions:	7in x 9in – Slide Valve
Hp: 5-7	*Rpm:* 100 *Psi:* 50
Service:	Supplied water for hydraulic presses.

This was in a general workshop which had once also been a forge and then later was a cloth processing shop.The engine was arranged to drive two ram pumps in the tank base through gearing and a Scotch crank. The gears could be disengaged to stop the pump when the engine could drive to the overhead shafting by a fast and loose pulley, making the engine usable for either or both purposes at the same time.

112 Leeds Industrial Museum, Canal Street, Leeds   SER 1492

Type:	Horizontal Tandem Compound
Photo taken:	1975
Maker and Date:	Wood, Baldwin? 1870s?
Cylinder/dimensions:	Approx. 10 and 20in x 3ft – Corliss and Slide Valves
Hp: 100	*Rpm:* 85 *Psi:* 120
Service:	Preserved; was chemical works and general plant drive.

This was Hardcastle's engine (see SER 1346) removed here when they closed. The museum site was Benjamin Gott's finishing mill, rebuilt after a fire in 1895. There were two large and a small water wheels, supplied from a large reservoir and the River Aire. Steam power was installed later, but nothing was known of this, and there have been such large alterations in the mill that the original layout is difficult to define. There are other engines to be exhibited include a Pollit and Wigzell uniflow engine, from Dobroyd.

113 The Hospital Laundry, Whitehall Road, Leeds   SER 1500

Type:	Horizontal Tandem Condensing Engine
Photo taken:	1974
Maker and Date:	Hick Hargreaves & Co., Bolton, No. 1174, 1896
Cylinder/dimensions:	12 and 24in x 3ft – Corliss Valves
Hp: 150	*Rpm:* 80 *Psi:* 150
Service:	Electricity supply to machine motors.

The site was Lupton's woollen mill and this engine almost certainly replaced a beam engine there. It was new to the mill from Bolton, and originally driving the mill shafts, now drives (1974) two generators by 6 ropes from the flywheel. It was Hick's standard engine in every way, with the valve boxes separate to the cylinder barrels which were plain cylinders with flanged ends bolted to the valve chest. The condenser vacuum was usually 24 ins. The laundry was due to move to a new site in 1977, but it was proposed to leave the engine in the mill, probably being the last engine at work in Leeds.

114 Longbottoms, Birstall, Leeds   SER 151

Type:	Single Cylinder Beam
Photo taken:	1935
Maker and Date:	Hoyle & Son, Halifax, c.1860?
Cylinder/dimensions:	25in x 5ft 0in – Slide Valve
Hp: 31	*Rpm:* 27 *Psi:* 10
Service:	Dye works. Gear drive to machine shafts.
	Beam 16ft 0in long. Flywheel 16ft 0in diameter.

A plain industrial engine that was unaltered in over 70 years of work. Little had ever been done to it, and it retained the long slide valve, with back packing strips to the end. The dyehouse load had greatly increased, so that the two boilers, at peak load, required two men, firing at under two minute intervals, to maintain 65 psi. The octagonal chimney, about 100ft high, had had a 30ft circular section added to it. The engine was scrapped in c. 1940.

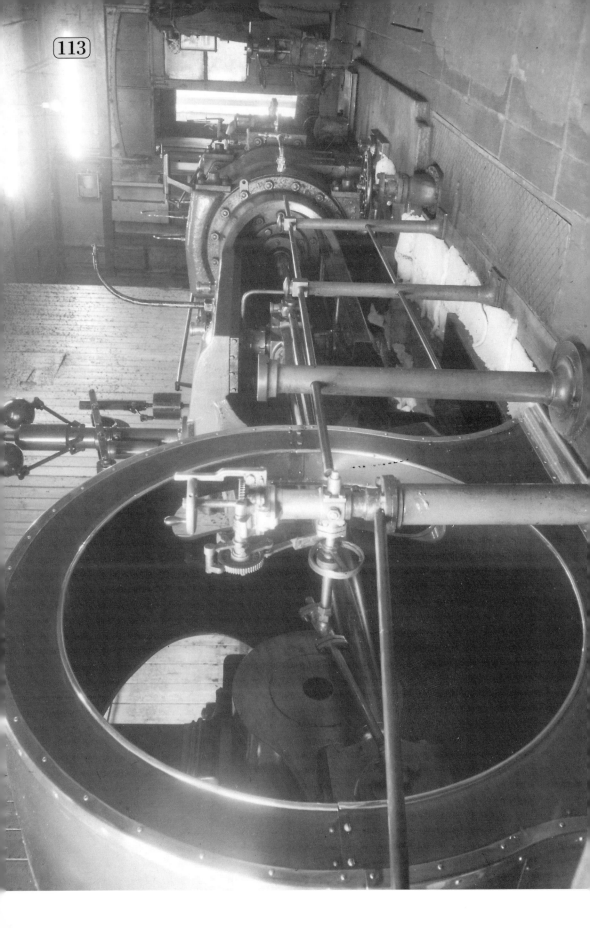

115 Maurice Dixon & Co., Canal Street, Leeds   SER 182

Type:	McNaughted Single Beam
Photo taken:	1937
Maker and Date:	Unknown
Cylinder/dimensions:	30in x 4ft 6in and 23in and 2ft 3in – Slide Valves
Hp: 140	*Rpm:* 40 *Psi:* 100
Service:	Works drive. Belt drive.

Nothing was known of the history of this engine by the engineer, who allowed unauthorized photographs to be taken. A new beam had been fitted apparently, but the cottered belts which held the beam centre bearing caps were retained with cotters in the pedestals, not the usual method of headed bolts up through the pedestals.

116 Hattersley & Co., Leeds   SER 183

Type:	Cross Compounded Double Beam
Photo taken:	1937
Maker and Date:	S & J Whitham, 1839
Cylinder/dimensions:	Approx. 30in x 5ft when built. 16in x 22in x 5ft as altered – Slide Valves
Hp: 120-140	*Rpm:* 32 *Psi:* 80
Service:	Textile spindle makers. Geared main drive to underground shaft by spur wheels 6ft 6in and 4ft 6in diameter. Beam 15ft 0in long Flywheel 15ft 0in

This had had a new flywheel, together with two new cylinders, but little else had been altered. It was a typical slight woollen area engine, yet it worked for a century with very little replacements other than the rebuild to use higher steam pressure.

117 J D Johnson & Co., Kirkstall Road, Leeds   SER 272

Type:	Single McNaughted Beam
Photo taken:	1939
Maker and Date:	Boulton & Watt, 1825
Cylinder/dimensions:	27 $\frac{1}{2}$ in x 6ft 0in – Slide Valve 23 1/4 in x 2ft 8in – Corliss Valves
Hp:	*Rpm:* *Psi:*
Service:	Woollen mill gear drive.

The insurance records stated that this was a Watt engine, and it was known to be a very old power site. No history of the changes was known, but it seems likely that two new cylinders were supplied in the 1903 rebuild, when it was McNaughted by Woodhouse and Mitchell. Otherwise little was altered structurally. The complex gearing layout remained until electric drives were installed in the late 1930s. The engine was scrapped in about 1939.

118 Kirkstall Forge, Leeds   SER 368

Type:	Undershot Water Wheel
Photo taken:	1951
Maker and Date:	
Cylinder/dimensions:	17ft 3in tip diameter x 2ft 6in wide
Hp:	*Rpm:* *Psi:*
Service:	Shingling and forging wrought iron. Hammer shaft cast iron approx. 9ft 0in long.

These were typical shingling helve hammers delivering slow heavy blows to expel cinder as well as general forging work. The cam or cog disc was about 26 inch diameter. The whole including the water wheel was very massive, almost entirely of cast iron. Believed to be preserved in situ. The stonework of the buildings was very fine.

119 George Lumb & Co., Wellington Mills, Elland, Leeds   SER 618

Type:	Inverted Vertical – Side by Side Compound. Condensing
Photo taken:	1953
Maker and Date:	Victor Coates & Co., Lagan Factory, Belfast, 1897
Cylinder/dimensions:	19³/₄in and 38in x 3ft 0in – Corliss Valves
Hp: 750	*Rpm: 99* *Psi: 160*
Service:	Woollen spinning. Rope drives off two flywheels.

This was overloaded and regularly developing over its designed power, and the mill had to be converted to electric drive for the further machinery then (1950) installed. It was the standard Coates design with the Corliss valve gear operated by eccentrics on the crankshaft and with ball and socket joints in the arms. The drive was taken off by rope driving wheels on either side of the engine, the whole being scrapped about 1960.

120 The Leigh Mills Co., Stanningley, Leeds   SER 697

Type:	Inverted Vertical Compound – Condensing
Photo taken:	1954
Maker and Date:	Pollit & Wigzell, 1917
Cylinder/dimensions:	18in and 36in x 3ft 0in – Drop inlet – Corless Exhaust Valves.
Hp: Approx. 600	*Rpm: 90* *Psi: 160*
Service:	Woollen cloth mill.

This was an economical engine which ran on superheated steam, and probably replaced a beam engine, but this was not certain. The condenser and air pump were on the engine room floor, with a large Baker's drum-type oil separator in the exhaust pipe. A Lumb governor was fitted in the 1920s, and although a good engine, it was for some reason not popular with the fitters who worked on it later. The mills were converted to electrical drive in the late 1950s, and the engine scrapped.

119

121 Robert Kaye & Co., James Street, Elland, Leeds   SER 840

Type:	Horizontal Single Tandem – Condensing
Photo taken:	1956
Maker and Date:	
Cylinder/dimensions:	9in and 18in x 2ft 0in – Corless Valves
Hp: Approx. 60	*Rpm:* 90 *Psi:* 140
Service:	Woollen cloth from raw wool. Gear drives.

The mill was old and long established for good blanket fabrics made entirely on the site, and comprised all of the woollen processes in one plant. The engine possibly superseded a beam engine, and was probably a single cylinder slide valve when erected in about 1860. It ran thus, and almost certainly had the condenser tandem on the end of the engine bed originally. It may well have been made by Wood Baldwin. In 1909 when the boiler was worn and more power was also needed, Woodhouse and Mitchell fitted the Corliss valve cylinders and the condenser was placed below, with the air pump driven off the crankpin. The original gear drives were retained, giving little trouble until the mill was closed in the late 1960s, a period of massive closures in the high grade woollen trade due to competition from man-made fibres. This engine had remained unaltered except for the features noted.

122 Job Beaumont & Co., Woollen Spinners, Linthwaite   SER 1490

Type:	Horizontal Tandem Compound
Photo taken:	1975
Maker and Date:	J & E Wood, Bolton, 1903
Cylinder/dimensions:	Approx. 16in and 30in bore and 3ft 6in – Corliss Valves
Hp: 450	*Rpm:* 80 *Psi:* 160
Service:	Drive mill machinery by ropes and alternator.

This replaced a beam engine when the mill was enlarged,and came new from the makers. It was the standard Wood engine, which originally drove the whole by 11 ropes to the room shafts; latterly much of the power was by an alternator and electric motors. The engine ran continuously through the day, a frequent procedure in woollen mills, and was especially stopped for the photograph to be taken. Regrettably the mills were closed in 1974 when the whole was scrapped except for the modern machines. The engine was very well kept and clean.

123 Hearl, Heaton & Co., Crown Street Works, Liversedge   SER 1233

Type:	Horizontal Single Cylinder – Non-Condensing
Photo taken:	1966
Maker and Date:	J B Clabour, Guiseley, Yorkshire, 1906
Cylinder/dimensions:	14in x 2ft 0in – Slide Valve
Hp: Approx. 40	*Rpm:* 100 *Psi:* 100
Service:	Works drive. Belt to main shaft.

This had driven the general steel fabricating small machinery for over sixty years, when the drives were converted to electric motors. It was a very compact little plant and the brick wall at the left was, in fact, the setting of the Lancashire boiler which drove the engine. The drive was by a belt pulley on the other side of the engine room wall, with a crossed 8in belt. The oval brass plate on the cylinder lagging stated her name *Rhoda* and maker. Other than a new Pickering governor fitted about 1965, little was altered, and there had been few repairs. It is preserved at the Bradford Industrial Museum at Moorside Mill.

124 The Heckmondwike Manufacturing Co., Liversedge   SER 1347

Type:	Horizontal Single Cylinder – Non-Condensing
Photo taken:	1968
Maker and Date:	Possibly J Clabour, Guiseley? 1890s?
Cylinder/dimensions:	8in x 1ft 3in – Slide Valve
Hp: 8-10	*Rpm:* 120 *Psi:* 100
Service:	Engineer's shop drive.

A general work-horse type of engine, heavy and simple, which was used daily as long as the engineering repairs were done by the staff. Latterly, with the shortage of good all-round tradesmen, the work was largely done by outside firms, and the engineer's shop was then driven by a motor. The workshop was still valuable for the small work that needed immediate attention, including much joinery and often sheet metal repairs.

125 Whitworth & Co., Cooperhouse Mills, Luddenden Foot   SER 57

Type:	Cross Compound Beam
Photo taken:	1936
Maker and Date:	Mill workshops?, c.1852
Cylinder/dimensions:	31in and 54in x 5ft 0in – Slide Valves (was twin 31in)
Hp: 600	*Rpm:* 32 *Psi:* 80
Service:	Wool spinning gear drive to $7^1/_2$in vertical shaft.
	Toothed flywheel rim to 5ft 0in pinion on second motion shaft.
	Room bevels 3ft diam. Beam 18ft 0in long. Flywheel 23ft 0in.

This was said to have been built in the owner's workshop, which was frequently done by large firms, which in the early days employed full maintenance staffs. Whitworths were a very large concern then, operating seven mills with eighty maintenance staff, so that the construction of an engine of this size was well within their capacity. The use of alternative mortise and iron toothed gearing throughout was a valuable refinement that gave very quiet working. The neat forged bosses on the connecting rods were typical Yorkshire details of the mid-19th century, the whole being a good example of pride of ownership. It was built as a double cylinder engine and compounded some 40 years later. The mill had also been water powered, the shaft of a suspension wheel about 15ft diameter x 16ft wide remained in the basement until the mill was finally dismantled.

126 Whitworth & Co., Cooperhouse Mills, Luddenden Foot   SER 57a

Type:	Horizontal Tandem
Photo taken:	1936
Maker and Date:	Pollit & Wigzell, Sowerby Bridge, date?
Cylinder/dimensions:	15in and 30in x 2ft 6in Stroke – Slide LP Valves
	Corliss HP Valves
Hp: 250	*Rpm:* 85 *Psi:* 150
Service:	Weaving shed engine. Rope drive.

This was a standard Pollit & Wigzell engine of the type that was met everywhere. It ran regularly until the business ceased in the 1940s. This, the beam, and another horizontal engine were all run off two Yorkshire boilers, probably installed in the 1920s. Every-thing was scrapped eventually.

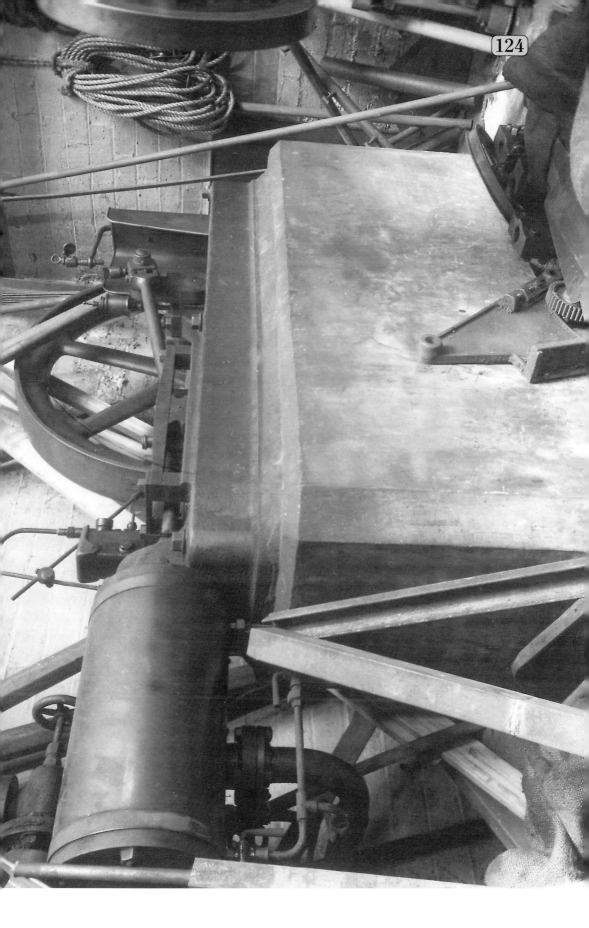

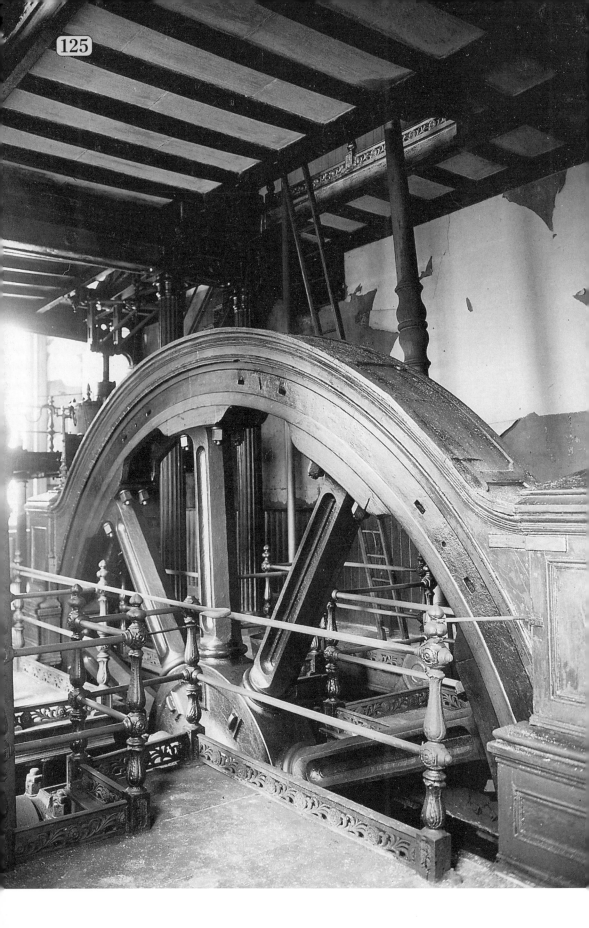

125

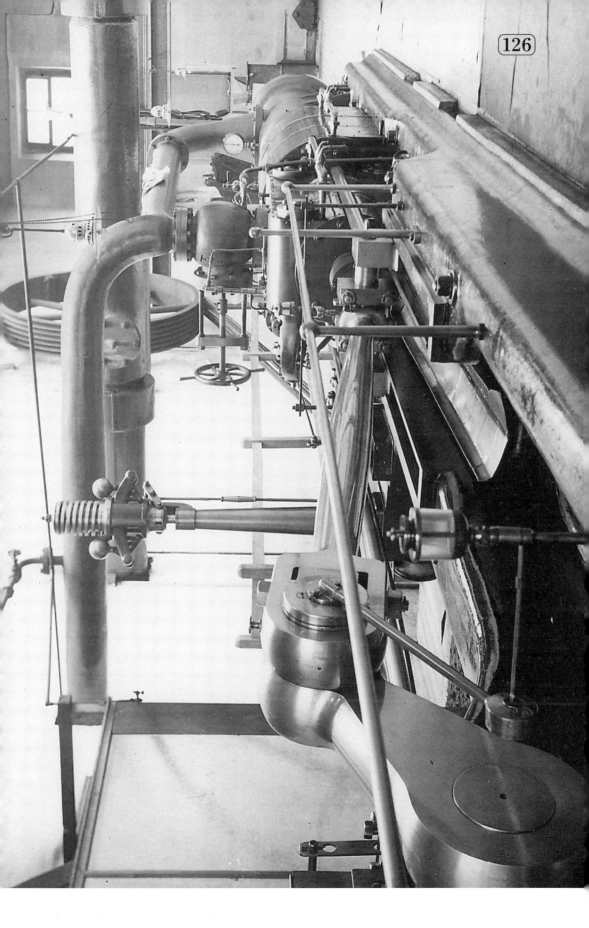

127 Fisher, Firth & Co., Cellars Clough Mills, Marsden   SER 1090

Type:	Single McNaughted Beam
Photo taken:	1962
Maker and Date:	Maker unknown – pre 1888.
Cylinder/dimensions:	28in x 6ft 0in and 20in x 3ft 0in – Corliss and Slide Valves.
Hp: 250	*Rpm:* 45 *Psi:* 100
Service:	Woollen mill drive. Originally geared then roped and then alternator and motors.

Nothing was known of the history before 1888, when Fisher, Firths took over, but the power was then from a water wheel 50 ft diameter by 12 ft wide, and the beam engine still possibly single cylinder, with gear driving throughout the mill. It was McNaught compounded by Woodhouse and Mitchell in the early 1900s, with a Corliss valve high pressure cylinder, and possibly a new low pressure slide valve at the same time. The gear drives were replaced by rope drives about that time and the plant ran so until it was decided to try all electric driving in the 1950s. An alternator was then installed, again driven from the beam engine, and the water wheel was replaced by a Gilkes water turbine. All of the shafting was removed and replaced by small electric motors. The change did not pay however, as the power lost was greater with the electrical transmission than it was with the ropes and shafts. Later, power was all taken from the Grid, but assisted by the Gilkes turbine and generator which contributed about 30 hp continuously. The beam engine was later presented to The Northern Mill Engines Society, who have removed it to Bolton for preservation.

128 Gjers, Mills & Co., Ayresom Ironworks, Middlesbrough   SER 1044a

Type:	Ironworks installation
Photo taken:	1961
Service:	Pig iron making.

The works were founded in 1870, and although the external appearance was not greatly altered, the power side was. Altered and modernised over the years, to the original three blowing engines, another was added by Yates & Thorn, and finally Westinghouse turbo blowers were installed of 1,080 h.p. each, possibly in the 1920s. The boiler plant was also greatly altered and from egg-ended boilers, later had 5 Lancashires and 12 Babcock and Wilcox water tube units. There was very great variation in the steam pressure which at times fell to 50 psi. By the 1950s the power system was again altered and the turbo blowers were not used. All four of the piston blowers were exhausting to a low pressure main to a 2,400 h.p. mixed pressure turbine generator in the power house. Although the original material hoists were retained, the furnaces were enlarged and some replaced. All was closed and scrapped about 1969.

129 Gjers, Mills & Co., Ayresom Ironworks, Middlesbrough   SER 1044b

Type:	Three Inverted Vertical – Non-Condensing
Photo taken:	1961
Maker and Date:	Maker unknown, 1870.
Cylinder/dimensions:	48in x 4ft 0in – Slide Valve
Hp: 150	*Rpm:* 30 *Psi:* 50-100
Service:	Blast furnace blowers. Steam cylinders above the 96in blowing tube.

These were the three original engines designed by Mr. J. Gjers for the works, but only two were installed initially. They were in use for many years, but latterly were assisted by the larger Yates & Thom engine, and later by the turbo blowers. The design was unusual and very compact, with the flywheels and four crankshaft bearings within the bed. They were designed as a unit as there were cross stays between the three engines, but only two were in use at once. The Yates & Thom engine was installed in the 1890s, and was a more usual type with the flywheels outside of the bed. The air pressure was $4^{1}/_{2}$ psi, and they were originally steamed by 6 egg-ended boilers 60ft. x 4ft. 6 inches diameter, which worked at 50 psi.

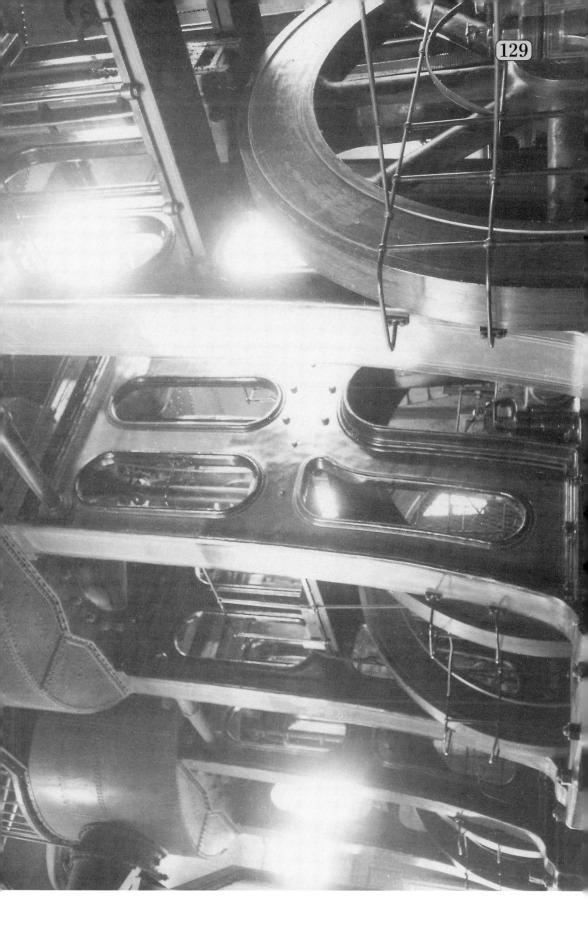

130 Dorman, Long & Co., Britannia Works, Middlesbrough   SER 1045

Type:	Horizontal Three Cylinder – Non-Condensing
Photo taken:	1961
Maker and Date:	Galloways, Manchester, c.1906?
Cylinder/dimensions:	36in x 4ft 3in – Piston Valves
Hp: 10,000 peak	*Rpm:* 120 *Psi:* 120
Service:	Rolling mill drive. Direct to mill. Exhaust steam to low pressure turbine.

This was Galloway's later design, very stiff and solid, with Joy's valve gear for the piston valves on top of the cylinders, and gave very good results in very hard usage. There was also a Davy Bros. twin cylinder cogging mill, and a Davy three cylinder vertical mill engine. All exhausted to the extensive power station which contained Metropolitan Vickers and A E G high pressure turbines and two A E G mixed pressure turbo generators of 2,750 kW each. The current was used to drive all of the works auxiliaries, as well as the No. 3 and 4 mills, each of which through flywheel generators took peaks of 6,000 h.p. per mill. There were 10 gas-fired Stirling boilers, and the storage regenerators for the turbines could store and discharge up to 117,000 lbs. of low pressure steam per hour. All was scrapped, when the mills closed, as the new plant came into production in the 1960s.

131 Dorman Long & Co., Acklam Steel Works, Middlesbrough   SER 989a

Type:	Two Horizontal Twin Tandem – Non-Condensing
Photo taken:	1959
Maker and Date:	W & J Galloway Ltd., Manchester, 1882 – Piston Valves
Cylinder/dimensions:	36in and 57in x 4ft 6in – Piston Valves
Hp: 4,000	*Rpm:* 80 *Psi:* 120
Service:	Steel rolling mill drive.

These had remained unaltered generally although there had been many heavy repairs during a long lifetime. The design was extremely massive, with a deep cast iron bedframe on either side from the crankshaft to the rear of the low pressure cylinder, which stiffened the engine greatly. The high pressure cylinders were not bolted to the bed bottom but only by a flange to the front of the main frame as can be seen below the driver's cabin. The piston valves were at the bottom of the cylinders.The output was general re-rolling material, i.e 2in square billets, as well as a large throughput of railway rails. The engines ran as long as the works were in action.

132 Dorman, Long & Co., Acklam Steel Works, Middlesbrough   SER 989c

Type:	Three Cylinder Horizontal Simple – Non-Condensing
Photo taken:	1959
Maker and Date:	W & J Galloway, Manchester, early 1900s?
Cylinder/dimensions:	36in x 4ft 3in – Piston Valves
Hp: 4,680	*Rpm:* 160 *Psi:* 120
Service:	Roughing mill drive. Direct to rolls.

Galloways later standard frame design was a very massive and deep casting on either side with the cylinders attached to faces upon the ends. The four bar crosshead guides were fitted to the inner side of the frame, with the crankshaft end of the frame tied by a massive cross casting. The valves were usually driven by Joy's valve gear, in this case with the piston valves below the cylinders, but the later ones had the valves on the top. Despite the heavy build, this engine had a fracture in the top bar of the crosshead guide of the left hand engine of the three (the patch can be seen). This engine was scrapped at the closure in the mid-1960s.

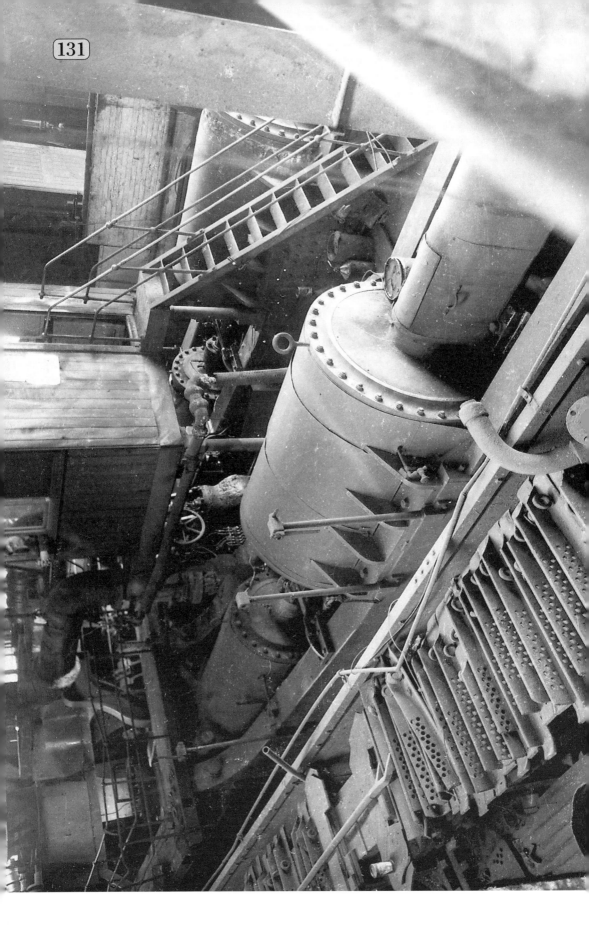

133 Dorman, Long & Co., Acklam Works, Middlesbrough   SER 989d

Type:	Horizontal Twin Cylinder – Non-Condensing
Photo taken:	1959
Maker and Date:	Davy Bros., Sheffield, c. 1890s?
Cylinder/dimensions:	40in x 5ft 0in – Slide, then Piston Valves
Hp: 3,000	*Rpm:* 90 *Psi:* 120
Service:	Cogging mill drive. Geared down 2 to 1.

This was very heavily worked as all of the steel had first to be cogged down to a smaller section before finishing in the other mills. This again had had several failures and repairs such as the heavy steel top plate upon the end of the bed near to the crank. The cylinders and bed were renewed in 1948, and this was the first major rebuild as the engine until then retained the original slide valve cylinders. In this design the drive was taken from between the cylinders, whereas in the other engines at Acklam the drive was off the end of the shaft. Starting from an ingot 18inch x 18inch x 5ft 0in long, the finished steel was over 270ft. long rails or $2^1/_2$ inch x $2^1/_2$ inch square. As rails, the final pass was 9 x 28ft. and 1x12ft. lengths. This took nearly $7^1/_2$ minutes in all, going through the three mills in turn.

134 George Lyle & Co., Ledgate Bridge Mills, Mirfield   SER 692

Type:	Pusher Compounded Beam
Photo taken:	1954 (Maker and date unknown)
Cylinder/dimensions:	$35^1/_4$in x 6ft 0in – Beam 19in x 6ft 0in – Horizontal
Hp: 400	*Rpm:* 42 *Psi:* 160
Service:	Woollen spinning.

Lyles took over the mill in 1879, and the engine then had a long history of ever increasing load. The engines were an addition to the original mill and were in a house built at the end. The main shaft was taken through the bottom floor to the original vertical shaft in the mill, which had probably been waterwheel driven originally. The horizontal engine drove by a crank pin in the gear driving wheel on the beam engine shaft, and the horizontal engine had been altered to give more power. The original slide valve cylinder was replaced by a Corliss valve for higher pressure. Still more power was needed, and new gears allowed the engine speed to be raised from 35 to 45 rpm. It ran until electrical drives were installed in the early 1960s.

135 George Lyle & Co., Ledgate Bridge Mills, Mirfield   SER 692 also

Type:	Single Cylinder Condensing Beam
Photo taken:	1954
Maker and Date:	Unknown, c.1860s?
Cylinder/dimensions:	$35^3/_4$in x 6ft 0in – Slide Valve
Hp: Approx. 200	*Rpm:* 42 *Psi:* 30
Service:	Mill drive.

Lyles possibly altered this engine in 1879 by attaching a horizontal engine. The beam engine had been much modified, to increase the power. Certainly the original cast iron beam failed in 1921-2, when the existing steel plate one was fitted in a general overhaul. A new cylinder was also fitted at some time by Woodhouse and Mitchell, together with a new connecting rod, but any possible original parts were retained, as the old eccentric rod was still in use. The history was hazy however, as Saxons were also said to have worked on it and even the date of the beam failure was uncertain. However, it remained at work until the conversion to motor drives, giving little trouble latterly. It was still in the mill although disused in 1971.

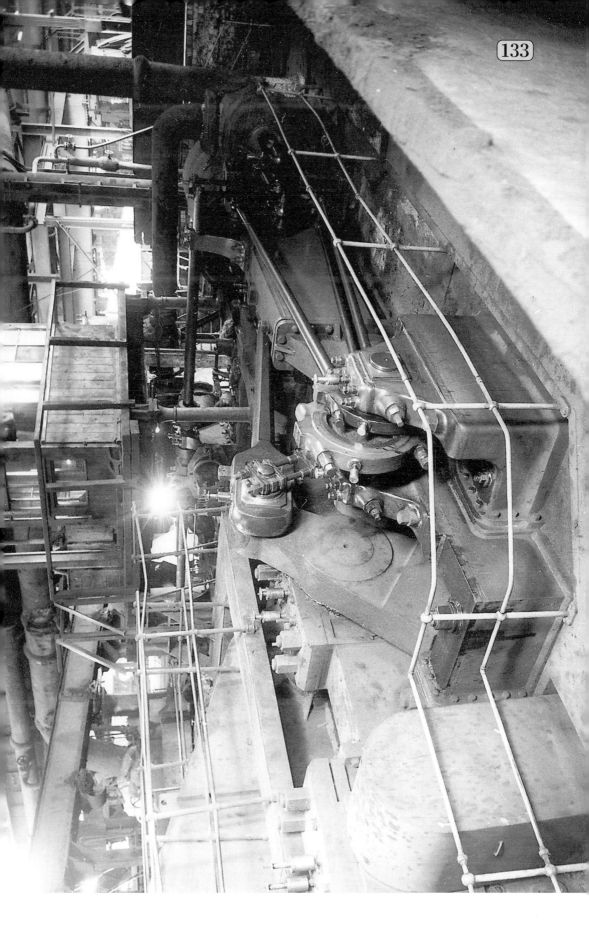

136 Walker & Co., Mirfield   SER 693

Type:	Horizontal Uniflow – Condensing
Photo taken:	1954
Maker and Date:	Marsdens Engines Ltd, Heckmondwike
Cylinder/dimensions:	Sizes unknown.
Hp: Approx. 350	*Rpm:* 130 *Psi:* 160
Service:	Woollen spinning and weaving.

This was the only uniflow that Marsdens made. It was moved from the original site (not known) to Walkers, by Mr R Inman in 1953, to drive the weaving shed by motors, and replace the existing gas engine. It was not greatly used however, and the load was put on to the Grid in the 1960s and the engine scrapped. Walkers had 3 other engines in 1956 all scrapped by 1972.

137 G F Walker & Co., Butt End Mill, Mirfield   SER 1401

Type:	Horizontal Single Tandem – Condensing
Photo taken:	1970
Maker and Date:	Marsdens Engines Ltd, Heckmondwike, 1927
Cylinder/dimensions:	15in and 30in x 3ft 0in – Corliss Valves
Hp: 350	*Rpm:* 92 *Psi:* 125
Service:	Woollen mill drive. 13 ropes off 10ft flywheel.

Christened *Edith Mary*, this was new in 1927 and replaced a beam engine. It was also coupled with two water turbines of 75 and 100 h.p. at the site, the water having provided the original power to water wheels, as the mill buildings were certainly old. The tandem drove on to the original main driving shaft of the beam engine which was in the house beside the tandem engine room, and so allowed the new engine to be installed with no interruption of the plant. It was a typical Marsden's design, and possibly one of their last tandems for a textile mill. It was certainly a very good one, and outside of the rebuilding of the bed beneath it in 1955, appeared to have needed little attention. There were two mill blocks and a weaving shed driven by the turbines and the engine but latterly the water power had fallen off with reduced water flow. The power was converted to electric motors in 1970 and the engine was to be scrapped. The drives were certainly extensive yet the friction loss was not excessive for the engine drove many machines as well as the looms.

138 J M Briggs & Co., Runtlings Mill, Ossett   SER 1468

Type:	Horizontal Tandem Compound – Condensing
Maker and Date:	Marsden's Engines Ltd., Heckmondwike, 1908
Cylinder/dimensions:	12in and 22in x 3ft – Corliss Valves and Slide Valves
Hp: Up to 120	*Rpm:* 75 *Psi:* 120
Service:	Mill drive. Roped alternator.

Named *Rhoda* and started working on April 13 1908, this engine was all that was left when the mill closed about 1974. All of the piston and valve rods were metal packed and had needed no repair for over 20 years. There was a single cast iron stay at the top between the HP and LP cylinders, whereas Marsden's usually used one cast with the bed, faced to bolt to lugs on the HP and LP cylinders. The bed, in two pieces, was nearly 25ft long. The mill was a single floor with one mainshaft about 125 ft long passing through 7 bays in the length. Six ropes drove off the 12ft flywheel to counter-shaft and alternator later (originally brought to main mill shaft). There is an overhead heater for mill water between LP cylinder and condenser.

139 Atkinsons, Foster Beck Flax Mill, Pately Bridge   SER 1084

Type:	High Breast Water Wheel
Photo taken:	1962
Maker and Date:	Tod Bros., Summerfield Ironworks, ?1900
Cylinder/dimensions:	35ft 0in diameter x 5ft 0in wide
Hp: Approx. 45	*Rpm:* $3^{1}/_{4}$ *Psi:* 30ft water head
Service:	Mill drive by spur ring and shaft.

This provided most of the power for the mill, with an oil engine to assist. The waterwheel was driven by a ring of internal teeth on the rim to a pinion about 5ft in diameter on the mill second motion shaft. This was geared up again inside of the mill, to make the main mill shaft speed 162 rpm, and the oil engine was coupled into this by a clutch and rope drive. The water wheel was well built, with 14 wooden arms about $5^{1}/_{2}$ inches square, with a rim segment, for containing 6 buckets for each arm. The side segments or shrouds, the hub, and the shaft, were all of cast iron but the soles of the buckets, i.e. the bottoms, were of timber 2in thick. It was a substantial structure which gave service with little repair for over 60 years when the flax mill was closed. The wheel was left in place as an attraction for visitors, when it was proposed to develop a tea garden on the site.

140 Wortley Forge, Nr Penistone (Founded 1713)   SER 353

Type:	Helve Hammers Three Water Wheels
Photo taken:	1950
Maker and Date:	
Cylinder/dimensions:	
Hp:	*Rpm:* *Psi:*
Service:	Axle forge.

This was the upper forge where the axles were finished, from the puddled iron made at the Low Forge, a mile or so away (which has now gone). Parts of the upper forge furnaces remain, together with the water wheels (largely of cast iron), whilst the hammers are almost complete. The two hammers were a spring type at one time. Both are of the belly type, i.e. with the cam ring between the pivot and the head, but the nearer one was replaced by the dead helve (acting by weight only) seen behind the crane.

141 Winterbottoms, Oxspring Wire Mills, Nr Penistone   SER 354a

Type:	Middle Breast Water Wheel
Photo taken:	1950
Maker and Date:	Unknown
Cylinder/dimensions:	14ft 0in x 5ft 0in
Hp:	*Rpm:* *Psi:*
Service:	Wiredrawers. Heavy drawing section.

This drove to the upper floor, through belt and gearing, with 5 or 6 heavy drawing blocks only, unconnected to the engine driven sets. The waterwheel is typical of the later wheels met in the Sheffield valleys, almost certainly of local make and with the exception of the bucket tips, was all of cast iron.

142 Winterbottoms, Oxspring Wire Mills, Nr Penistone   SER 354b

Type:	Drawbenches
Photo taken:	1950
Maker and Date:	
Cylinder/dimensions:	
Hp:.	*Rpm:* *Psi:*
Service:	Wiredrawers. Light draft benches.

There was an auxiliary steam engine, which was geared to the lower set of benches nine in a row and also drove another set at right angles, by a shaft under the floor. There was also a belt drive to the upper floor from it, to 5 or 6 light blocks, in line with the water driven heavy ones. The works was re-organized later and the whole of the older plant was scrapped.

143 Pontefract & Goole Waterworks, Roall Pumping Station SER 1077

Type:	Two A Frame Woolf Compound Beam
Photo taken:	1962
Maker and Date:	Easton and Anderson, Erith & London, 1891
Cylinder/dimensions:	14in x 3ft 0in and 22in x 4ft 0in – Slide Valves
Hp: ?	*Rpm:* 20 *Psi:* 120
Service:	Town supply from wells.

This represents the last phase of Easton and Anderson's beam engine design, very plain and practical, with a single web beam and a jaw end for the connecting rod, conical cylinder covers, and rectangular cast iron connecting rod. The cylinders and covers were fitted with steam jackets.There were two engines installed end to end in the same house, but one was removed, and a diesel driven well and surface lift set installed in its place which could pump most of the available water. The remaining beam engine was very well preserved and neatly painted, and well kept as seen in the 1960s .

144 Pontefract & Goole Waterworks, Eggborough Pumping Station   SER 1078

Type:	Two Inverted Triple Expansion
Photo taken:	1962
Maker and Date:	Hathorn Davey & Co., Leeds, 1933
Cylinder/dimensions:	Approx. 12in – 18in and 28in x 2ft 0in – Drop Valves
Hp: Approx. 90	*Rpm:* 20 *Psi:* 220
Service:	Town supply, single well pump to each engine. One million gallons per day, approx. 250ft. lift.

This plant although very efficient was little used until it was scrapped in about 1967. There was a single well pump driven from a crank at the end of each engine, to a bell crank at the well which was outside the engine house. There was a separate well for each engine. No positive data was available for the plant. The engines were in line along the house, and were steamed by two J. Thompson's Cornish boilers with corrugated furnaces. They were almost certainly the only ones made to work at the pressure of 220 psi, and superheat. The furnaces were 3ft 6in diameter and the shells were 6ft diameter by 21ft long. One of the engines was later altered to run from an electric motor. There were the usual surface lift ram pumps beneath each of the cranks, and driven from the crossheads.

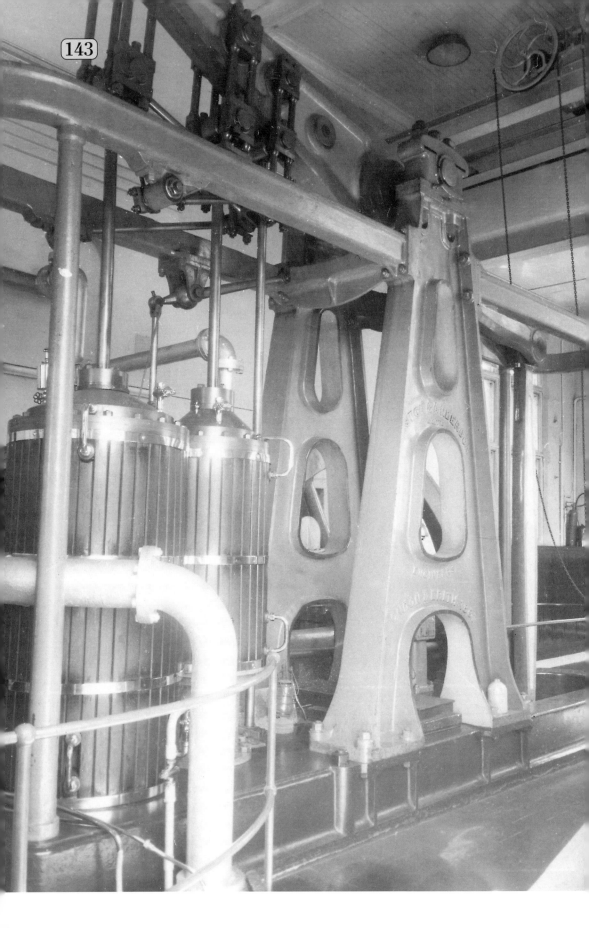

145 Pontefract and Goole Waterworks, Brayton Pumping Station,   SER 1079

Type:	Two Inverted Vertical Triple Expansion
Photo taken:	1962
Maker and Date:	James Watt & Co., 1906
Cylinder/dimensions:	13in – 20in and 34in x 2ft 0in – Corliss Valves
Hp: 70 each	*Rpm:* 27 *Psi:* 150
Service:	Town supply from wells 150 ft. deep.

Dated 1906, which was long after Watt's works were closed, this was probably finished by Avery's who bought the Watt premises. They were plain but efficient units, which had considerable use. There was a single well pump at the end of each engine, with a surface lift ram pump beneath each crank driven from the crossheads. There were four crankshaft bearings, with no couplings between the cranks, and the well pump was driven by a crank on the outer side of the flywheel. The plant boilers, engines and pumps cost £32,000, and pumped 1,000,000 gallons per day for many years. There were at least two installations of engines by James Watt & Co dated well after the official closure of the works by the receivers in 1896 (see SER 666). The whole station was intact in 1963.

146 The Prince of Wales Colliery, Pontefract   SER 1344

Type:	Horizontal Double Cylinder
Photo taken:	1968
Maker and Date:	Walker Bros., Wigan, 1912
Cylinder/dimensions:	38in x 7ft 0in – Drop and Corliss Valves
Hp: ?	*Rpm:* 45 *Psi:* 80
Service:	Coal winding. Shaft 640 yds deep. Rope Drum 12ft diameter (was 18ft).

This was said to have been bought second hand from Llay Main pit in North Wales in 1938, possibly when the Markham engines were installed there, although this did not fit the opinions at Llay. It made 34 revolutions per wind latterly, as the original drum had been replaced by a smaller one with the intention of converting it to electrical drive. Steam was given for 23 of the 34 revolutions the wind required, but the cut off was under governor control, and came into operation after the four revolutions of the engine. There were 11 Lancashire boilers for 150 psi, which served the large power house with mixed pressure turbines, two with alternators, and one with an air compressor. A large electric winder was being installed in 1968 to deal with all the coal. The other winder was a Bradley & Craven, 1910, fitted with new cylinders for 150 psi directly from the boilers. There was also a Bellis engine driving the fan, but all was to electric drive later.

147 G Hartley and Foster, Union Bridge Mills, Pudsey, Nr Bradford SER 1001

Type:	Horizontal Single Cylinder – Condensing
Photo taken:	1959
Maker and Date:	Marsden's Engines Ltd, Heckmondwike
Cylinder/dimensions:	18in x 3ft 6in – Corliss Valves
Hp: 150	*Rpm:* 84 *Psi:* 80
Service:	Woollen mills. Drive by 14in belt off flywheel rim.

There was a pair of water wheels originally, and these were replaced by a beam engine possibly around the 1860s and this ran until *Edith May* was made and installed by Marsden's in 1919. It was economical, although the mill gearing was quite extensive, since the little plant produced grey woollen cloth from raw wool, although there was no washing or dyeing. The engine was heavily built and gave little trouble other than a cylinder re-bore and new piston by the makers in 1956. All of the load was due to go to electric motors in the early 1960s, and by 1963 this was well in hand, but the mill closed before the electrical drives were complete and the whole was scrapped. The single boiler was secondhand in 1928, from a mill that was closed.

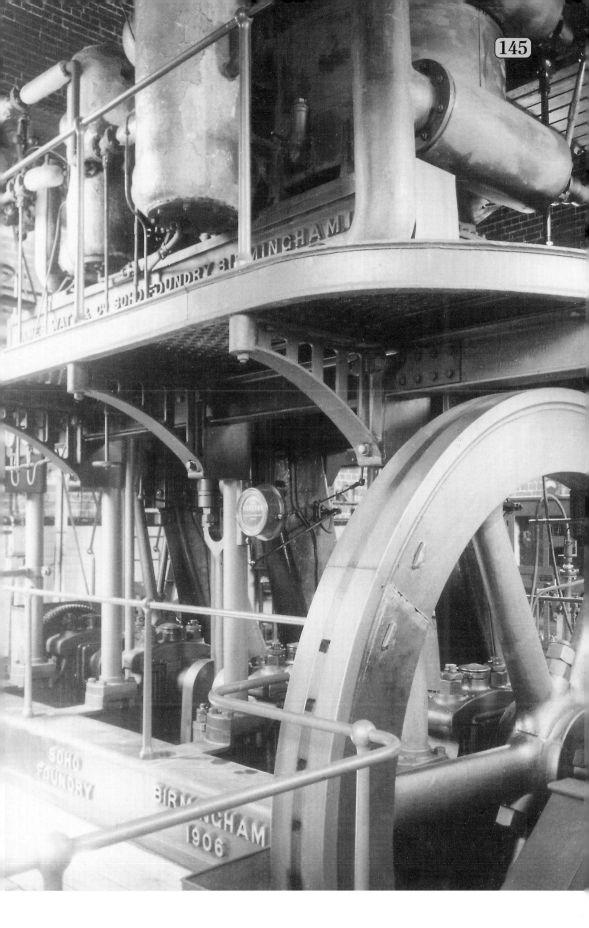

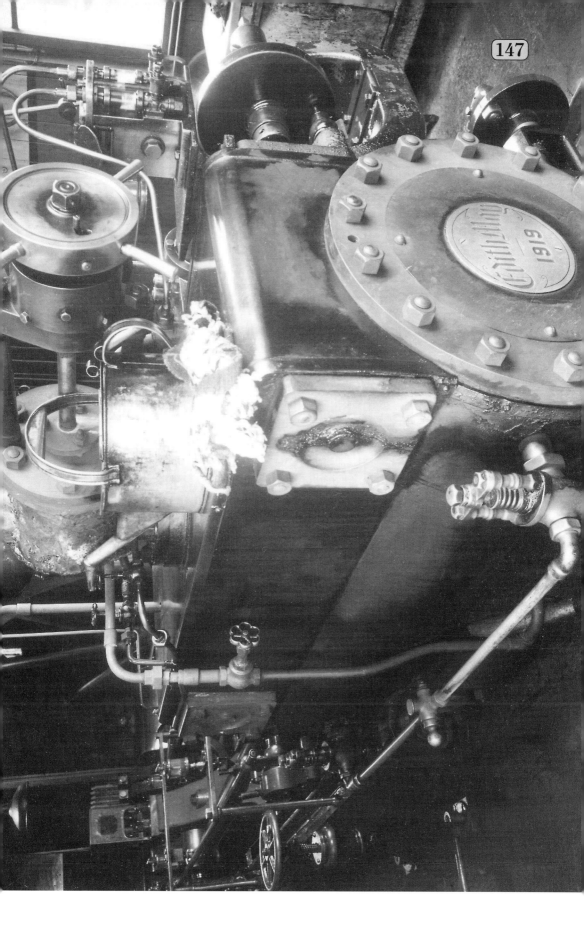

148 Mohn & Co., Alma Tannery, Pudsey   SER 1351

Type:	Horizintal single cylinder – Non-condensing
Photo taken:	1968
Maker and Date:	Newton, Bean & Mitchell, 1926
Cylinder/dimensions:	$16^{1}/_{2}$ in x 2ft 0in – Corliss Valves
Hp: Approx 120	*Rpm:*120 *Psi:* 160
Service:	Plant drives by alternator. 5 ropes off flywheel.

The works were converted to electric drives in the 1920s and the engine installed to provide current for this and exhausting into the process steam lines, which assisted the heating processes. Most of the current used came from the Grid, but this engine greatly assisted by relieving the day-time loadings. It stopped working in 1970 with other re-organising. One major incident was a piston rod failing at the cotter hole in the cross-head in the 1950s. This fractured the cylinder head and piston, but the makers repaired it and it was running again in under two weeks.

149 Helms and Co., Spout Mills, Rastrick   SER 1130

Type:	Horizontal single tandem
Photo taken:	1963
Maker and Date:	Woodhouse and Mitchell, 1924
Cylinder/dimensions:	16in and 32in x 3ft 6in – Corliss valves
Hp: 600	*Rpm:* 80 *Psi:* 150
Service:	Woollen manufacturers. Approx 12 ropes from 14 ft flywheel. Finest cloth from raw wool tops.

This was made especially to fit the smaller engine room of the 500 hp Woodhouse engine which was sold to Bucktons, Leeds, and had a shorter stroke than was usual for a 600 hp. The mills were built in 1889, with many gear drives but these were all converted to rope drives later, and latterly there were over 100 separate ropes in all. It was very efficient, with only small gear drives to the second motion and a small floored section. The whole was due to be sold by auction when the mills closed in 1965, and the engine was almost certainly scrapped.

150 John Smith & Co., Badger Hill Mills, Rastrick   SER 997

Type:	Horizontal single tandem – Condensing
Photo taken:	1959
Maker and Date:	Wood Bros., Sowerby Bridge. 1911
Cylinder/dimensions:	13in and 26in x 3ft 6in
Hp: 250	*Rpm:* 80 *Psi:* 140
Service:	Woollen mill drive. Rope drives to several mill shafts.

This was almost certainly supplied new to the mill and ran regularly until the drives were converted to electricity in the early 1960s. It was generally unaltered and needed little repair, but a Lumb governor was fitted new in 1953. It ran on superheated steam and was quite economical, but with growing loads and new electrically driven machinery, the drives were converted to motor drives entirely in the early 1960s when the engine was scrapped. There were very few Wood Bros' horizontal engines of this type left in later years, but this was typical of their work.

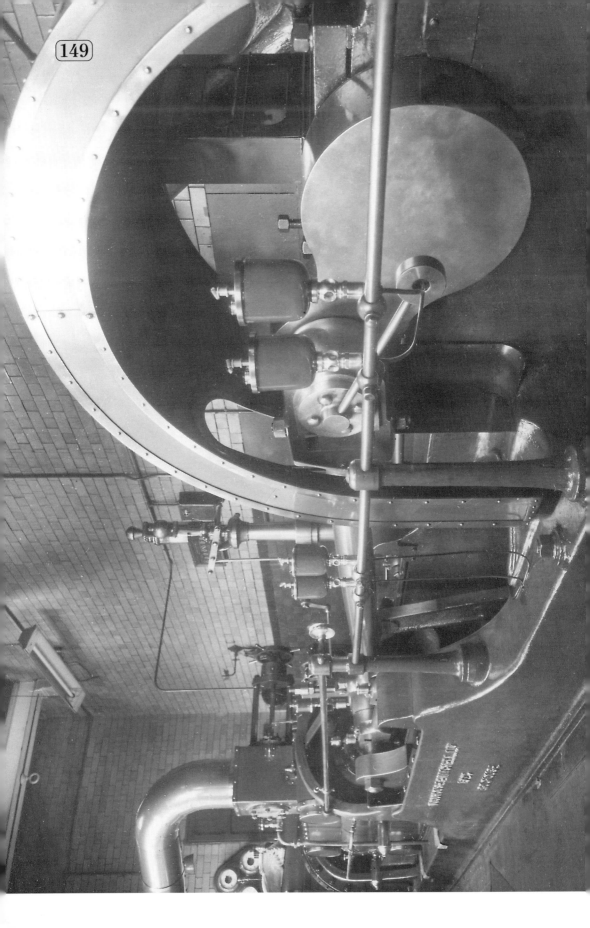

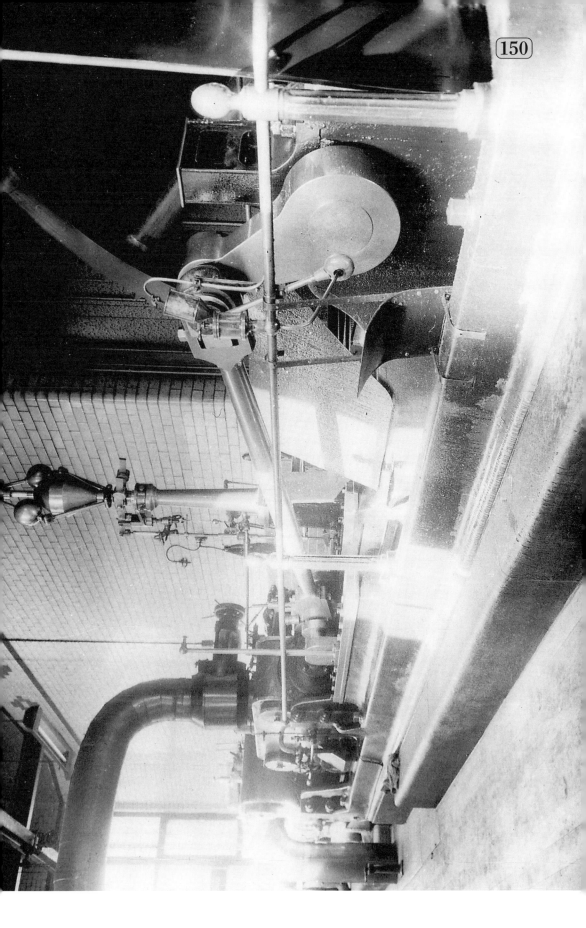

151 Rockingham Colliery   SER 627

Type:	Double cylinder vertical – non-condensing
Photo taken:	1954
Maker and Date:	Lilleshall Co., 1895
Cylinder/dimensions:	36in x 6ft 0in – drop valves
Hp: ?	*Rpm:* 30 *Psi:* 100
Service:	Coal winding. Round ropes; drum 18ft 0in diameter.

The cast iron "A" frames were very massive but all of the motion structure, i.e. parallel motion was light, and stiffened with stays across the beams. It was fitted with Allan link motion, which drove the drop valves by a layshaft at mid-cylinder level below the engine room floor. The engine house was massive and of stone, and this plus the engine had needed no more than routine attention in some 70 years of heavy work until the colliery closed in the 1950s.

152 Steel, Peech & Tozer Ltd., Rotherham   SER 1039a

Type:	Twin inverted vertical simple expansion
Photo taken:	1961
Maker and Date:	Hick, Hargreaves & Co., Bolton, 1914
Cylinder/dimensions:	20in x 2ft 3in – piston valves
Hp: 800	*Rpm:* 120 *Psi:* 120
Service:	Steel railway tyre mill. Roughing stage.

These were high speed enclosed and forced lubricated engines, driving the mills by couplings at the end of the crankshaft, for the first and second forming stage mills for the blank tyre rings. One engine drove the inner, and the other the outer forming roll for the blank. A light balance wheel was fitted to the crankshaft between the two engines which were coupled together. Each engine was provided with a Berry, steam engine driven, three-ram hydraulic pump, which can be seen by the officer on the right. The plant was hard driven, and very well maintained. All of the engines were non-compound and non-condensing, since very rapid handling was required for full capacity. The mill was replaced by a large automated unit in the 1960s.

153 Steel, Peech & Tozer Ltd., Rotherham   SER 1039b

Type:	Horizontal twin cylinder – Non-condensing
Photo taken:	1961
Maker and Date:	Yates and Thom, Blackburn, 1914
Cylinder/dimensions:	24in x 3ft 6in – Corliss valves
Hp: 1,000	*Rpm:* 100 *Psi:* 150
Service:	Tyre finishing mill.

This drove the mill by underground shafting and gearing, and was very heavily used. It was well maintained and when cylinder wear developed some years after it was in-stalled, the steelworks staff made and fitted the piston tail rods, which were very effective in reducing the wear. The clean condition was its every day state, a tribute to all concerned since it was open to the mills, with dust everywhere. Steam was provided by three Economic type boilers, which served the mills and services by the steam main over the engines.

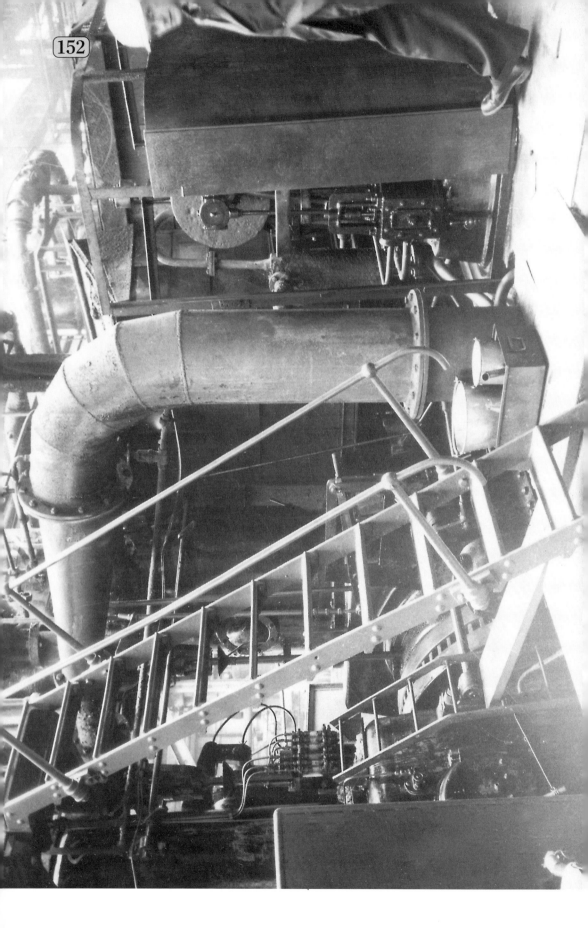

154 The Park Gate Iron & Steel C., Rotherham   SER 1385

Type:	Two horizontal double cylinder
Photo taken:	1969
Maker and Date:	Berry & Co., Leeds c.1900
Cylinder/dimensions:	Not known – Slide valves
Hp: ?	*Rpm:* 40 *Psi:* 80
Service:	Hydraulic power for general works use.

Hydraulic power was extensively used for manipulating the hot metal in the rolling mills, for traversing rolled sections to the correct grooves in the rolls, and turning it for the same purpose. It was extremely valuable for this work where instant and accurate control was essential. The low steam pressure and continuous starting and stopping of the engines made twin high pressure cylinders essential, as the engines were entirely controlled by the position of the accumulator rams which stored the water under pressure. The two engines, one by Berry seen in the photograph, and the other by Markham's, varied widely in their details, but the principle was the same, plain twin steam cylinders that would start anywhere, with the pumps tandem and the whole mounted on a single bedplate. The pumps were twin plunger type off each tail rod. The entire works was scrapped under Nationalisation.

155 The Park Gate Iron & Steel Co., Rotherham   SER 1385a

Type:	High speed, three cylinder compound
Photo taken:	1969
Maker and Date:	Belliss and Morcom, Birmingham, No 4278
Cylinder/dimensions:	Sizes unknown
Hp: Approx. 800	*Rpm:* 400 *Psi:* 80
Service:	General plant service. (Other plant see Nos 733 and 993).

The use of electricity developed from lighting, to small isolated motors for cranes etc., and for this the small capacity of the Bellis engine was sufficient until, with the development of the works main power station with steam turbine blowers for the blast furnaces, and generators for the rolling mills, the Bellis was only supplying direct current for cranes. The low works auxiliary steam pressure – 80 psi – did not make triple expansion worth while, and the compound was ample. It was superseded by an AC to DC generator, but was retained in the works' power house in case of need. It was not much used in the 1960s, but, well kept, was available when needed. The three cylinders gave even turning with good overload capacity.

156 The Park Gate Iron & Steel Co., Rotherham   SER 993a

Type:	Horizontal, twin tandem – Non-condensing
Photo taken:	1959
Maker and Date:	W & J Galloway, Manchester, 1912?
Cylinder/dimensions:	Two 38in and two 57in x 4ft 6in ? – piston valves
Hp: 8,000	*Rpm:* 90 *Psi:* 90
Service:	Steel rolling, 24in mill. Exhaust steam to low pressure turbo generators.

This was purchased from Coleville's Scottish steel works in the 1930s and was erected in 1941, after a long period on the site. It was W & J Galloway's usual design with very stiff main framing, but not with the single lever control system they later developed. The piston valves were on the top of the cylinders, with twin valves for the low pressure, all driven by Joy's reversing gear. The mill was used for roughing and finishing, and reversed up to 10 times in two minutes, with 3-4 revolutions per pass in the early roughing stages and up to 21 at the end of the finishing runs. It was directly coupled to the mill and had done a great deal of work at Park Gate. The cylinders were all renewed by Hick, Hargreaves about 1950, and new pistons later. It was scrapped with the rest of the works upon Nationalisation, after 1964.

156

157 The Park Gate Iron & Steel Co., Rotherham   SER 733d

Type:	Horizontal three cylinder, simple expansion, reversing
Photo taken:	1955
Maker and Date:	Markham and Co., 1911
Cylinder/dimensions:	36in x 4ft 6in – piston valves
Hp: 8,000	*Rpm:* 140 *Psi:* 160
Service:	Finishing mill.

This and the Galloway (see previous photograph) were mainly for finishing stages. The Markham was very similar to Galloway's three cylinder designs, with massive mono-lithic bed and frame, Joy's valve gear and the piston valves on top of the cylinders. It had the usual replacements that the heavy duties demanded, rolling mills could not be kept low on maintenance but the general massiveness of this one certainly made for reliability. The clean condition of the engines was the everyday situation, remarkable since the engines were in the mill itself, not in the engine rooms, and so were in the dust and heat, quite close to the rolling mills. The Markham was direct hydraulic, not steam hydraulic reversed, the rams being seen at the right hand outer side of the bed.

158 The Park Gate Iron & Steel Co., Rotherham   SER 733c

Type:	Horizontal three cylinder, simple expansion, reversing
Photo taken:	1955
Maker and Date:	Lamberton & Co., Coatbridge, 1911
Cylinder/dimensions:	All 40in x 4ft 6in – piston valves
Hp: 10,000	*Rpm:* 120 *Psi:* 160
Service:	Billet mill drive.

This was a typical Lamberton with Allan link motion and piston valves at the side. Each engine had a separate bed structure. This was fitted with new main bearings in 1958, and was massive and well built in every way. The duty of this and the Davy Bros. next to it, was the roughing mills drive which was very heavy work. The Davy was replaced (when Shotton Steel works superseded their billet mill engine) by the Scott and Hodgson (see SER 688) three crank from Shotton, when it was superseded by an electrically driven mill.

159 The Park Gate Iron & Steel Co., Rotherham   SER 733d(2)

Type:	Horizontal, three cylinder, simple expansion
Photo taken:	1955
Maker and Date:	Markham & Co., Chesterfield, 1911
Cylinder/dimensions:	36in x 4ft 6in – piston valves
Hp: 8,000	*Rpm:* 140 *Psi:* 160
Service:	Steel rolling, 24in mill; direct coupled.

This was purchased new, and installed directly to increase capacity. It was the maker's very stiff design, with short framing, and massive construction, with piston tail rods and the valves on top of the cylinders. Usage was very heavy, but it had given relatively little trouble. The crosshead guides were fitted to bearing points in the framing, and generally was very simple with four bearings only for the crankshaft. Working billets 8in x 8in x 14ft long, it rolled these to various finished sizes in about $1\frac{1}{2}$ minutes, and made 18 passes of metal through the rolls, reversing each time. This also exhausted to the exhaust steam turbines and was scrapped on Nationalisation.

160 The Park Gate Iron & Steel Co., Rotherham   SER 733f

Type:	Horizontal twin tandem, double acting, gas driven
Photo taken:	1955
Maker and Date:	Worthington Simpson (Snow design), 1920
Cylinder/dimensions:	24in x 4ft 0in, double acting
Hp: approx 1,400	*Rpm:* 50 *Psi:?*
Service:	Furnace gas driven blowing engines; air tube: 59in pistons.

There were two engines, one made by The Snow Co. of New York, and the other by Worthington made to replace the other Snow engine lost in transit during World War 1. Both of the engines were standby to the main steam turbo blowers, one gas engine always being kept running on light load, so that blast would not fail if a steam set stopped. The general demand made gas engines less attractive later, when other uses were found for the gas, and they were also very costly to repair in breakdowns, but these were very rare at Park Gate.

161 Kilnhurst Colliery, Rotherham   SER 187

Type:	Cornish-type beam
Photo taken:	1937
Maker and Date:	Mare & Co., Plymouth, 1843
Cylinder/dimensions:	36in x 7ft 0in ?
Hp:	*Rpm:* *Psi:*
Service:	Pit pump, no data.

This was very little used in 1937 and no data was available. It was however, largely a standard type. Early design features were the criss-cross moulding of the parallel motion filler blocks and the neat rib moulding forged on the centre of the parallel rods. It was scrapped in c. 1940.

162 J W Wheelwright & Co., New Mill, Rishworth   SER 58

Type:	High breast waterwheel
Photo taken:	1936
Maker and Date:	Taylors of Marsden
Cylinder/dimensions:	57ft 6in diameter x 12ft wide
Hp: 240	*Rpm:* 2 *Psi:*
Service:	Cotton spinning; spur gear drive off wheel rim 54ft diameter.

This was the largest waterwheel in use for many years, and was the mainstay of the mill power until the closure. A double beam engine was installed to assist it in low water periods, the two being coupled into the same vertical shaft system. It was a suspension type wheel with 174 non-ventilated buckets, each of which held 12 cubic feet of water. There were 120 arms to keep it in shape, and the whole weighed 70 tons. It contained 28,000 (sic) pieces in all, and it was said that it took 29 horses to haul the cast iron shaft to the site over the local hills. It was fitted with wooden buckets in the late 1930s, since they were simpler to install than the shaped steel ones would have been. The mills were later used by Crossley Carpets and they retained the waterpower by a turbine and generator. The beam engine was replaced by a vertical compound; see *Textile Mill Engines* p186 and plate 43

163 Scarborough Waterworks, Irton Station   SER 113

Type:	Two single cylinder rotative beam
Photo taken:	1935
Maker and Date:	Bradley & Craven, Westgate Common Foundry, Wakefield, 1884
Cylinder/dimensions:	28in? x 5ft 6in drop – valves
Hp: ?	*Rpm:* 18 *Psi:* 55
Service:	Town supply. Well & surface lift. 1 million galls per day, 300-500ft head per engine. Beams 22ft 0in long. Flywheel 15ft 0in diameter.

Probably the last remaining beam engine by the makers, but no works remained in 1950. The high lift pump was driven directly from the beam near to the connecting rod, with a pump for lower town service, driven by a disc crank on the end of the crankshaft. The cast iron connecting rod was very slight, and the mahogany wood lagging was especially fine and well maintained. Standby to electric pumps in 1938, they were retained during the 1939-1945 War, and probably scrapped c.1948.

164 Scarborough Waterworks, Osgodby Station   SER 114

Type:	Bull engine
Photo taken:	1935
Maker and Date:	Kitson & Co., Leeds, 1871
Cylinder/dimensions:	45in x 9ft 0in
Service:	Town supply from well to reservoir. Ram force pump off piston rod, with side rods to bucket pump in well.

This was a plain engine, of interest for the equilibrium valve being placed at the top of the cylinder, instead of in the usual point beside the steam valves. The surface condenser was immersed in the balance tank between the well and the surface pumps. The whole was placed over the well, with the ram pump on girders, and with side rods from the crosshead down to the well pump. This was retained as a standby during the 1939-1945 War, an advertisement for a driver appearing in the local press in 1939. It was scrapped in c.1950.

165 The English Steel Corporation, River Don Works, Sheffield   SER 1040

Type:	Inverted vertical three cylinder simple
Photo taken:	1961
Maker and Date:	Davy Bros., Sheffield, 1905
Cylinder/dimensions:	40in x 4ft 6in – piston valves
Hp: 12,000	*Rpm:* 120 *Psi:* 160
Service:	Drive for 48in plate mill.

This was removed from Cammell's works about 1954 and was later coupled to the high pressure (400 psi) steam system of the works power station, through an accumulator and reducing valve system. The engine was very powerful and was geared down 1 to 4 to the mill. Handling was rapid, and an ingot 26 inches thick was reduced to $2^3/_4$ inches thick with thirty three passes through the rolls in nine minutes, and it could work an 80 ton ingot down to a plate 40ft. long x 13ft. wide and 3in. thick in a single heat. The rolls weighed 40 tons each. Joy's radial reversing gear was fitted, handling was fast, and the engine framing was massive, with the reduction gear framing integral with the engine bed, all being joined by deep flanges. The mill was to be retained on steam drive in the 1960s as there were few which could do the heavy work, which was not sufficient to justify costly electrification.

164

166 George Clarke & Co., Sheffield   SER 1042

Type:	Horizontal single cylinder gas engine
Photo taken:	1961
Maker and Date:	Crossley, Manchester, early 1900s
Cylinder/dimensions:	Approx 15in x 1ft 9in
Hp: 100	*Rpm:* 150 *Psi:*
Service:	Steel re-rollers; mill drives by 5 ropes.

Clark's used gas engines extensively for the rolling mill drives, with town gas. Although more costly, they were very reliable and needed little attention. They were not over-loaded as a rule and this was a help, with heavy flywheels. Certainly they gave very good results, far better than many attempts to use gas engines for steel rolling, and at Clark's engines had been installed as the business developed, there being 4 or 5 finally. They were replaced as they aged and greater powers were needed, and this was the last one in use, in 1960. It was then due to be retained in service for a year or two, and later was replaced by a heavier electrically driven mill bought secondhand, with a motor about 400 h.p. Increasing capacity in this way allowed other mills to be disused, and the result was good. It was a tribute to the engines and the management, that the results were as they were. The engine was scrapped afterwards.

167 The English Steel Corporation, Stevenson Road Works, Sheffield.   SER 1073

Type:	Three cylinder horizontal simple expansion.
Photo taken:	1962
Maker and Date:	Lamberton & Co., Coatbridge, 1904
Cylinder/dimensions:	32in x 4ft 0in piston valves.
Hp: 5,000	*Rpm:* 120 *Psi:* 120
Service:	Steel rolling, reversing and non–condensing.

A typical Lamberton reversing mill engine, this was fitted with Allan link motion, with each engine line separate in contrast with the closely placed frames of the later Galloway and Markham designs. It had had two new crankshafts, one in 1927, and another in 1939 following a bend in that of 1927. Three new cylinders were fitted together with pistons by Lockwood and Carlisle about 1946. Metallic packing was not fitted to the piston and valve rods until 1959. The engine weighed nearly 165 tons in all. It exhausted to a mixed pressure turbo-generator and was steamed by coal and oil fired Economic-type boilers, usually three working and one standby, together with waste heat boilers on the ingot soaking pits, the latter producing nearly one third of the total steam. The engine was scrapped in a modification of the works in the 1960s.

168 Wragg & Co., Refractory Clay Products, Loxley Valley, Sheffield   SER 1168

Type:	Horizontal single cylinder non - condensing.
Photo taken:	1964
Maker and Date:	Thornewill & Warham, Burton on Trent., 1924.
Cylinder/dimensions:	20in x 3ft 6in., drop inlet – Corliss exhaust.
Hp: 200	*Rpm:* 80 *Psi:* 120
Service:	Mill Drive.

This drove directly on to the mill main drive shaft and replaced another engine. The works boilers were dated 1907 and 1915, both by Davy Bros., Sheffield. The trip gear for the inlet valves was unusual, resembling a Corliss rather than a drop valve type, but worked very well. It was massive and well made and had needed very little attention for many years. It was repainted with maroon coloured paint in 1945, and this was still as good as ever 20 years later. The exhaust steam was used in the drying chamber floors and it certainly paid its way. However it is probable that it was replaced by a motor in the 1970s.

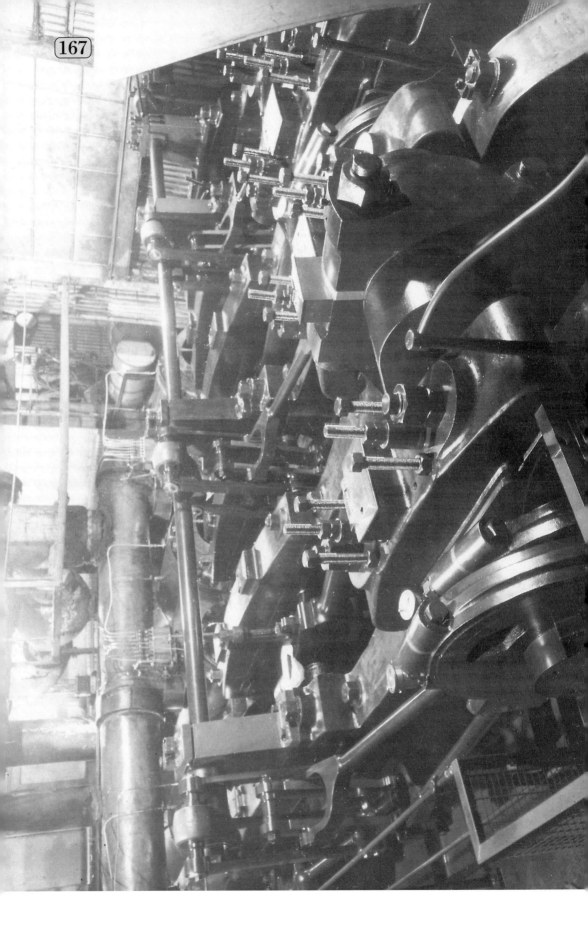

169 The Wardsend Steel Co., Sheffield. SER 1169

Type:	Horizontal cross compound condensing.
Photo taken:	1964
Maker and Date:	Davy Bros., Sheffield, Pre–1894.
Cylinder/dimensions:	18in and 36in x 4ft 6in – Corliss valves. 1924.
Hp: Approx. 400	*Rpm:* 65 *Psi:* 120
Service:	Rolling mill drive by helical tooth gearing – ratio 2 to 1 down to rolls.

This was almost certainly built with slide valve cylinders and originally drove by a 26in wide belt to three mills. The cylinders were replaced by those seen made by Ashton and Frost, Blackburn in 1924, and possibly new boilers were supplied then. The mill drives had been greatly altered, as originally the engine drove three sets of rolls by a 26in belt to two and a gear train to the third mill. Latterly (1948), two mills were driven by a separate motor, leaving one gear-driven train on the engine. The entire plant was dismantled and all was scrapped except the new motor and gear box which were moved to another site.

170 Tyzack Son and Turner, Little London Works. Sheffield.   SER 1469

Type:	Forged blanks showing the stages from steels to finished blade.
Photo taken:	1974

On the left are three pieces, a heavy top and bottom of mild steel to support the thin piece of shear or tool steel in the centre. This was welded into a single mass and drawn to a long shank in one "heat" and then reversed and the other end welded and drawn as in piece 3 from left. Piece 4 shows the initial tool shape, thinning it to expose the tool steel centre and leaving the thick mild steel back to support it. The first 4 stages were performed in the welding, the next 4 in the plating "fire". The last two, finishing the "tang" for fitting the handle was the last working stage, after the edge and sides were part ground, and the whole tempered and hardened. Other than grinding, all of the forming was by heating, and a good "heater", who could keep the forger supplied as fast as he was ready for a blank, was as important as the forger himself. Modern processes are a steel centre, with a folded soft steel "back" slipped over and rivetted. It involves much less heating, but tempering and grinding are necessary.

171 Tyzack Son and Turner, Little London Works, Sheffield.   SER 1469a

Type:	Forging hearth for welding and plating edge tools.
Photo taken:	1974
Service:	Edge tool forge.

The forge contained 2 fires, that on the right for welding the initial three pieces of metal into one, and roughly shaping it as a blank, and the plating furnace on the left, which could contain the blank as it gained in length and width into the finished blade. The fire was contained in the two rectangular holes seen in the front, and were simply brick lined boxes without fire grates and with forced draught inlets on the outer sides. The top continued as a horizontal duct to a short vertical flue discharging into the hood. The made-up steel blanks were inserted in holes in the flue, and moved forward as each heated blank was inserted in the very hot front hole over the fire. Each bundle of 3 steel pieces made two tool blanks, forged under the tilt hammer in several "heats", or reheatings. For plating, or forging into a thin wide blank ready for grinding and finishing, the blade was inserted in the front top hole only, being now too long to go side ways in the flue. The great heat made heavy clinkers, which were cleared by taking off the cast iron front plates and pulling them out.

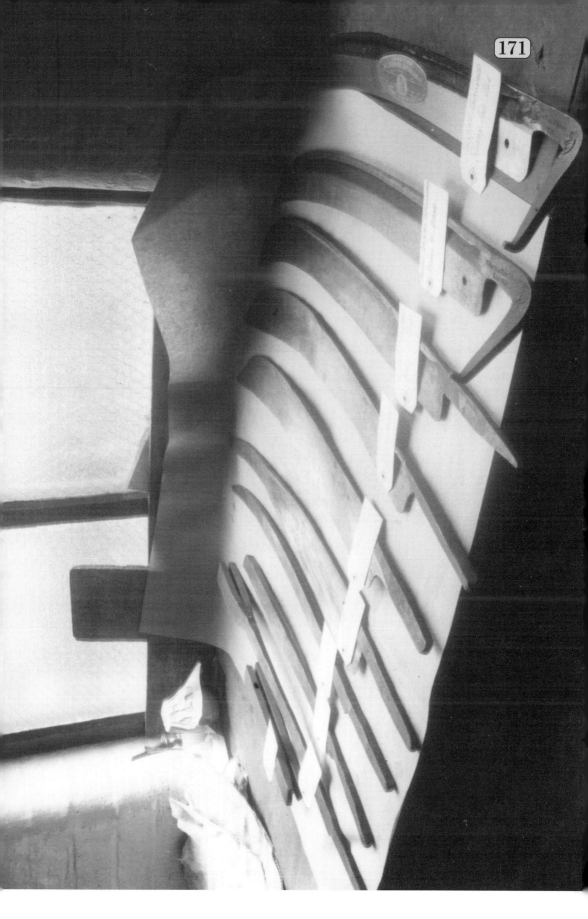

172 Tyzack & Turner, Little London Works, Sheffield   SER 355a

Type:	Middle breast water wheel.
Photo taken:	1950
Maker and Date:	Unknown.
Cylinder/dimensions:	15ft x 5ft 6in.
Hp:	*Rpm:* *Psi:*
Service:	Tool forge. Tilt hammers.

This was in use until about 1950, and even later for small special orders whilst the craftsmen were available. It was probably the last working tilt forge in the city. It contained the usual welding and plating hammers and had a separated blowing wheel at one time. Each water wheel was built in four sections, with two arms to each, wedged on to the cast iron axle. This was continued through to carry the hammer cam rings.

173 Tyzack & Turner Ltd., Little London Works, Sheffield   SER 355b

Type:	Tilt hammers for plating and welding tools.
Photo taken:	1950
Maker and Date:	
Cylinder/dimensions:	
Hp:	*Rpm:* *Psi:*
Service:	Edge tool forge. Preserved?

Typical Sheffield edge tool forge driven by gearing from 355a (see above). Octagonal cast iron main shaft which, as well as the tilt hammers, drove the bar shears at the left and the grindstone for the tool faces. The left hand hammer was in use, showing the forgeman's swinging seat, and the wooden rod by which he controlled the water to the wheel. The cloths on the hammer shaft were wetted to prevent shrinkage, the can on top having a small hole through which water dripped to keep the cloths moist. The use of an old bevel wheel as a flywheel was interesting. The tongs on the right hand anvil show the steel (soft top and bottom with a shear steel centre for the edge) ready for welding.

174 Kayser, Ellison & Co., Carlisle St, Sheffield   SER 255

Type:	Twin cylinder rotative beam.
Photo taken:	1938
Maker and Date:	Walker, Eaton & Co., Spittal Hill? 1870?
Cylinder/dimensions:	24in x 7ft 0in – Corliss valves.
Hp: 6–700	*Rpm:* 18–20 *Psi:* 110
Service:	Rolling mill.

This was completely rebuilt by Ashton, Frost & Co., in 1907, when they fitted new cylinders, steel plate beams, new connecting rods, and probably a new crankshaft. This may have been due to an accident, but could have been a part of a general works reconstruction. It was very economical, and regularly ran on a single Lancashire boiler in later years, until increasing demands led to new mills and drives. The drive was by gear to the second motion shaft from which a heavy mill was once driven, and then by ropes to the finishing mills, latterly the only drive, and using the whole power of the engine. It was scrapped in a reorganization of about 1960.

175 The Abbeydale Forge, Sheffield   SER 256

Type:	Forge blower and tilt hammer.
Photo taken:	1938
Maker and Date:	
Cylinder/dimensions:	
Hp:	*Rpm:* *Psi:*
Service:	Tilt hammers etc.

This was the main unit for welding and plating the rough blanks, and the size can be estimated from the gear wheel which was 15ft 0in diameter and the flywheel, which was 13ft 0in. The two piston blowers were overhead, driven by cams on the water wheel shaft. Although they seem so close, the tilts and the blowers had separate water wheels and were quite independent.

176 Sheffield Forge & Rolling Mill Co., Millsands, Sheffield   SER 336

Type:	Double beam engine.
Photo taken:	1947 (sic) [but ?1946]
Maker and Date:	Walker, Eaton & Co., 1855 & 1860?
Cylinder/dimensions:	$31^5/_8$ in x 5ft 0in – drop valves $33^1/_2$ in x 6ft 2in.
Hp: 800	*Rpm:* 30 *Psi:* 80
Service:	Rolling mill drive.

This was waterwheel driven until about 1850, when the smaller of the engines was put in to work with the water power. The smaller of the two engines was installed about 1860 to replace the water power, being bought secondhand. It was completely different from the other engine, in sizes, and design, but they worked well together. Sinkage of the foundations gave much trouble with the increasing loads of later years, when a sheet mill as well as a heavy billet and rod mills were added. The whole plant was remodelled in the late 1940s, when forging was abandoned and all of the several steam drives were replaced. Even so, one electrically driven mill with a very good motor of about 1914, whose non-standard current needed a special transformer even in the 1950s. The beam engine was scrapped in 1946.

177 Sheffield Forge and Rolling Mills, Millsands, Sheffield   SER 356b

Type:	Horizontal single cylinder non–condensing.
Photo taken:	1950
Maker and Date:	Unknown
Cylinder/dimensions:	25in x 4ft 0in – slide valve.
Hp: 60	*Rpm:* 70 *Psi:* 100
Service:	Rolling mill drive.

This drove two small stands of rolls for special sections, plus small parcels and orders. The flywheel was massive but otherwise it was undistinguished, and regularly used when small orders came in. The rolls were readily changed to meet needs, serving a useful purpose, yet requiring little attention in return. In the early 1950s, the character of the business and the plant were changed, the forge being abandoned, and gradually the steam plant was replaced by electrically driven mills of different types. The business was still active as re-rollers until Nationalisation.

178 W. A. Tyzack & Co., Clay Wheel Forge, Sheffield   SER 357

Type:	Overshot waterwheel.
Photo taken:	1950
Maker and Date:	J. Rhodes, Owlerton, Sheffield – c1850?
Cylinder/dimensions:	10ft 0in diameter x 4ft 0in wide.
Hp:	*Rpm:* *Psi:*
Service:	Edge tool works drive.

This was an independent forge in regular use in the 1950s on special types of edge tools, mainly for agricultural use, i.e. bill hooks, scythes, axes, etc. There were two water wheels, and this, the smaller, drove only the blowers for the forge fires, and the larger one (seen at the left) drove the tilt hammer. It is probable that the whole plant dated from 1850, but little information was available. The plant was typical of the independent small works, often with a world-wide connection for specialities, yet only employing 8-10 men. Most of such plants closed in the 1950-60 period, when no young hands came in to be trained in this small but highly skilled trade.

179 Sheffield Forge & Rolling Mills Co. Millsands, Sheffield   SER 356c

Type:	Horizontal single tandem condensing.
Photo taken:	1950
Maker and Date:	Brightside Engineering Foundry & Co., Date unknown.
Cylinder/dimensions:	Approx. 16in and 30in x 3ft 0in – piston valve H.P.
Hp:	*Rpm:* *Psi:*
Service:	General rolling mills drive.

This again was a general service small rolling mill, but was a much more fully used engine than SER 356b (above), and of a highly sophisticated design. It was fitted with a separate cut-off valve to the high pressure cylinder, which was under governor control and fitted with a jet condenser. Unlike SER 356b, this was running continuously with good economy due to the cut-off control and condensing operation.

180 Messrs. Eaton, Booth & Co., Bradfield Rolling Mills,
Owlerton, Sheffield   SER 358

Type:	Overshot waterwheel.
Photo taken:	1950
Maker and Date:	13ft 0in diameter x 6ft 3in wide–maker and date unknown.
Cylinder/dimensions:	No other data.
Hp:	*Rpm:* *Psi:*
Service:	

This plant had had several changes in product, having once made edge tools. Latterly it was rolling very high grade steels for the aeronautical industry, having one reverberatory furnace, and reducing steel billets about one inch square down to $5/_8$in by $1/_8$in several passes but without reheat which would have spoiled the steel. The waterwheel drove through double speed-increasing gearing, with a massive flywheel upon the high-speed roll shaft, the latter giving great steadiness of speed despite the length of steel in the final passes. The little plant with a few hands was thus able to compete effectively with the large plants, and work off small parcels that were a nuisance to a large establishment. Closure again was probably due to no hands following on the trade.

179

181 John Wood & Co. Wisewood, Nr Sheffield   SER 383a

Type:	Waterwheel and piston blowers.
Photo taken:	1951
Maker and Date:	Maker unknown, date possibly 1850s
Cylinder/dimensions:	Waterwheel 12ft 6in diameter x 5ft 0in wide.
Hp:	*Rpm:* *Psi:*
Service:	Tool forge.
	Numerous small forges and several steam hammers.

Plain high breast waterwheel with cast iron arms and rim sectors, and wrought iron buckets, geared to the blower shaft. This was later replaced by a water turbine and used for many years until others replaced the piston blowers. It was all scrapped in the early 1960s because the floor was unsafe.

182 John Wood & Co., Wisewood, Nr Sheffield   SER 383b

Type:	Twin double acting square piston blowers.
Photo taken:	1951
Maker and Date:	Date and maker unknown. c.1850
Cylinder/dimensions:	Pistons 26 in square x 3 ft 0 in stroke 20 double strokes per minute.
Hp:	*Rpm:* *Psi:*
Service:	Blower for tool forge blast.

Positive pressure blowers providing blast for numerous furnaces and open fires for tool forging. The pistons were supported at the rear as well as the crosshead, and were packed with square strips of rhinoceros hide and graphite. Three flap type inlet and one similar outlet valve were fitted at each end of the cylinders. Each valve was 9 in x 7 in, with leather facings. The air was delivered to the blast main by a 9 in diameter circular cast iron pipe. A Root's blower rather than fans may have replaced these blowers in the 1940s.

183 Wortley Low Forge, Nr Sheffield.   SER 384

Type:	Waterwheel driven belly helve hammer
Photo taken:	1951
Maker and Date:	Unknown
Cylinder/dimensions:	Waterwheel approx.15ft 0in diameter x 2ft 4in wide.
Hp:	*Rpm:* *Psi:*
Service:	Working scrap iron for axle and general forgings.

The waterwheel was undershot, and the whole plant very massive, and almost exclusively of cast iron. Wortley was a wrought iron plant, latterly working up scrap iron into blooms to be finished as railway axles at the Upper Forge (see SER 353). The Low Forge had comprised a complete iron plant with beam engine driven rolls, steam hammer, and a new rolling mill was installed but little used when Wortley closed about 1925. The whole was very derelict by 1954, even the buildings being dismantled. The large timber beam broken on the top was 22ft 0in long and some 24in square.

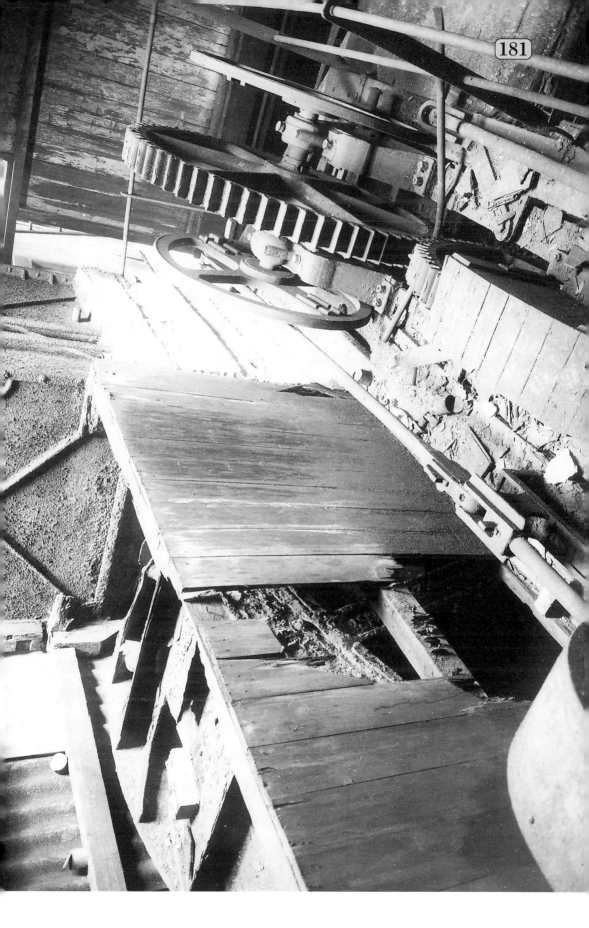

184 Sanderson, Newbould & Co., Attercliffe, Sheffield   SER 922

Type:	Two horizontal tandem compound.
Photo taken:	1958
Maker and Date:	W & J Galloway Ltd., Manchester. 1914
Drop valves.	
Cylinder/dimensions:	$17^1/_2$in and 33in x 3ft 6in – drop valves.
Hp: 500	*Rpm:* 72 to 120 *Psi:* 150
Service:	Steel rolling. 14 rope drive on each.

The plant was very well kept, and the photographs were taken when re-flooring was in progress, hence the temporary timber floor. The trip gear was Galloway's standard type which they used prior to the development of the Pilling oil valve gear about 1920. The engines were condensing with the condenser tandem to the low pressure cylinders and both engines drove backwards to the rolling mills, which were 10in and 14in diameter and running at 120 to 200 rpm Three Lancashire boilers by Davy Bros., Sheffield were installed, two of which were used, driving the engines, and steam hammers for billet forging, the office heating and other loads. The engines were side by side in the engine room. New electrically driven mills were installed in the 1960s, replacing the above.

185 Fisher, Firth & Co., Shepley New Mills, Shepley   SER 1154

Type:	Inverted vertical triple expansion.
Photo taken:	1964
Maker and Date:	Wood Bros. Sowerby Bridge. Approx. 1906?
Cylinder/dimensions:	15in–22in and 34 x 3ft 6in – Corliss valves.
Hp: 600	*Rpm:* 85mill drive by 16 ropes to alternator.

This. was made for Joseph Rank's flour mill at Hull, probably about 1906 and removed later to make room for a larger Wood Bros' engine. It was then installed at Eli Whiteley's Mill, Sowerby Bridge, and ran this until the mill was closed about 1936. It was then purchased by Fisher, Firth & Co for about £250, and installed at Shepley with the alternator, to drive electrically so replacing the McNaughted beam engine and gear drives. The consulting engineer said this would not save anything in total costs, and this proved to be the case, but the old engine and gearing were badly worn and had to be replaced. Bulk supply from the Grid came below the cost of on-site generating by 1962, and grid current was purchased, but the engine was retained and was very useful later, keeping the mill running in the power cuts.

186 Benjamin Armitage & Co., Shepley   SER 1237

Type:	Horizontal cross compound.
Photo taken:	1966
Maker and Date:	Schofield and Taylor, Huddersfield 1907.
Cylinder/dimensions:	13in and 24in x 3ft 0in – Corliss and slide valves.
Hp: 250	*Rpm:* 80 *Psi:* 130
Service:	Mill drives by 7 ropes off 13ft flywheel. Latterly mainly to alternators.

This was designed to develop 130 hp at 65 rpm and steam at 80psi With need for greater power, the engine was speeded to 80 rpm and to use 130 psi which nearly doubled the power. Further changes in later years led to the wide use of electrical drives in scattered parts of the mills. The alternator was 80 hp and the weaving shed was always driven by a single 56 h.p. motor, which was made in 1901, but installed much later here. A new Lumb governor was fitted in 1958, when complete conversion to electric drive was prepared for, but in the end the current was purchased from the Yorkshire Grid system. The engine, however, was kept running into the late 1960s, feeding current into the system, but it was shut down by 1970, and may have been scrapped. The high pressure cylinder was named *Benjamin*, the low pressure being named *Martha*.

184

187 Morrisons, Orbic Works, Shipley.   SER 1152

Type: Horizontal single tandem.
Photo taken: 1964
Maker and Date: Maker and date unknown.
Cylinder/dimensions: 12in and 24in x 3ft 0in approx.
Hp: 120   *Rpm:* 96   *Psi:* 100
Service: Works drive by 6 ropes off 10ft flywheel.

This appears to be parts of several engines, and different builders. The trunk frames resembled several makers practice, the high pressure cylinder is certainly by McNaughts of Rochdale, the low pressure almost certain to be Pollit and Wigzell, and the circular condenser greatly resembles Newton Bean and Mitchell's design! It is the results that count, and this engine ran 140 hours per week as long as recollection went, certainly well over 30 years, and appeared likely to continue. The engineer was certainly a good man, neglecting nothing and, considering its continuous running, it was well kept. There are in fact few chances to clean it. It was running in 1973.

188 Butterfield & Fraser, Cottingley, Nr. Shipley,   SER 1348

Type: Horizontal single tandem condensing.
Photo taken: 1968
Maker and Date: J. & W. McNaught, Rochdale.
Cylinder/dimensions: 15in and 32in x 5ft 0in – Corliss and slide valves.
Hp: 350   *Rpm:* 85   *Psi:* 120
Service: Works drive 12 ropes off 18ft 6in flywheel.

This replaced an engine in the room beside it, and was purchased from Speight and Co., Bradford to whom it was supplied new, but no dates either of the building or sale are known – it is not in McNaught's list. It now has Marsden's trip gear (and possibly the whole cylinder was made by them), but again no dates are known. It certainly had some thirty years of work at Cottingley, until electrical driving was installed in the 1960s, the engine being finally removed about 1970. A simple, plain engine, there was little to suggest a maker, but other than the high pressure cylinder, few modifications or repairs had been made to it.

189 Stuart Bros., Shipley   SER 62

Type: Single cylinder condensing beam.
Photo taken: 1936
Maker and Date: Coles Marchent & Co., Bradford, 1856?
Cylinder/dimensions: 27in x 5ft 0in – four slide valves
Hp: 100   *Rpm:* 32   *Psi:* 50
Service: Wool carbonising gear drive off the flywheel arms.
                           Beam 15ft 0in long Flywheel 18ft 0in diameter.
                           Engine stopped about 1954 and scrapped 1961.

This engine was fitted with Varley's valve gear which comprised separate slide valves for the inlet and exhaust, for each end of the cylinder. The four valves were driven by a vertical shaft at each side of the cylinder, but a unique feature was that the inlet shaft at the left side revolved at one half of the engine speed, whilst the exhaust shaft at the left ran at engine speed. Another interesting point was that the inlet valve shaft was driven intermittently, since it was coupled to the cross shaft by two oval wheels, which gave an alternate dwell and rapid drive. This was valuable as the valve was stationary when it was open or shut, but moved rapidly when it was opening or closing. There was a throttle and governor only.

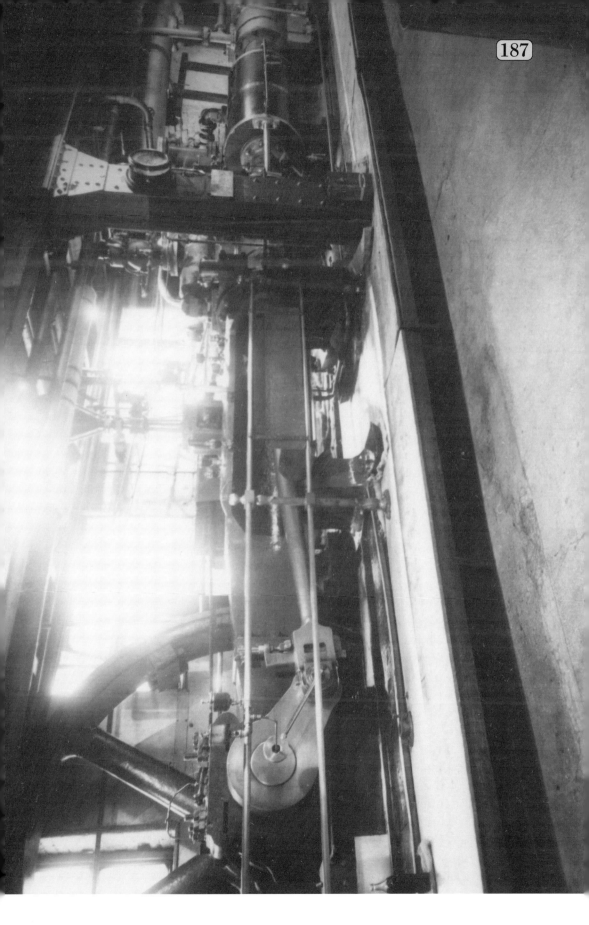

190 Taylor's Woollen Mills, Silsden, Keighley   SER 1150

Type:	Inverted vertical cross compound.
Photo taken:	1964
Maker and Date:	Scott and Hodgson, Guide Bridge 1896.
Cylinder/dimensions:	17in and 35in x 4ft 0in – Corliss and Piston valves
Hp: 700	*Rpm:* 75 *Psi:* 160
Service:	Mill drive by 15 ropes and 3 to weaving shed.

This was built for Union Mill, Audenshaw, and was moved to Silsden in 1917 to replace the beam engine and gear drives. It was installed in a new house to give length for the rope drives. A new Hewett and Kellett boiler for 160 psi, with superheat to 180° F was installed at the same time, which was still insured for the same pressure in 1964. It is a typical Scott's engine, with slight connecting rods, long stroke piston valve for the low pressure cylinder, and with Scott's method of fitting the flywheel to the crankshaft with a bored fit and two tangenical keys. It was still running in 1973.

191 Lumb & Co., Paper Mills, Skyreholme   SER 163

Type:	High breast water wheel, disused 1937 & scrapped 1940
Photo taken:	1935
Maker and Date:	unknown
Cylinder/dimensions:	39ft 0in diameter x 5ft 6in wide
Hp: Approx. 100	*Rpm:* 45ft head of water. *Psi:*
Service:	Possibly woollen mill once? No positive history known.

Built entirely of iron this probably dated from the mid 19th century. The rim was in twelve sections, each containing 9 buckets. The gear driving ring was, however, made in 18 segments all bolted to the side of the bucket segments, with a wooden packing, 1in thick beneath the ring of teeth. The whole was suspended by 12 sets of radial arms, $1^3/_4$ in diameter which were attached to the hub by threaded ends and nuts. The gear drive to the mill shaft gave a total increase ratio of 30 to 1. It was superseded by a 200 hp oil engine in the 1930s.

192 Crowther & Co, Titanic Mill, Slathwaite   SER 1074

Type:	Horizontal single tandem.
Photo taken:	1962
Maker and Date:	Mark Shaw, Milnthorpe – 1912
Cylinder/dimensions:	18in and 38in x 5ft 0in – Corliss valves.
Hp: 450	*Rpm:* 75 *Psi:* 120
Service:	Woollen spinning. 8 rope drive.

This was contracted to be built for £1020 and was made to J and E Wood's drawings, but a little more was finally paid, since there were a few modifications made in building it. It was identical with Wood's design in every way and could have made little profit for the builder. It drove the large long mill, from a central rope race, by two ropes per floor, and there were four floors. The drive was changed to electric motors about 1967, when the engine was scrapped. Copying such an engine without patterns must have been very costly, and it is doubtful if Wood's patterns were available for its construction.

191

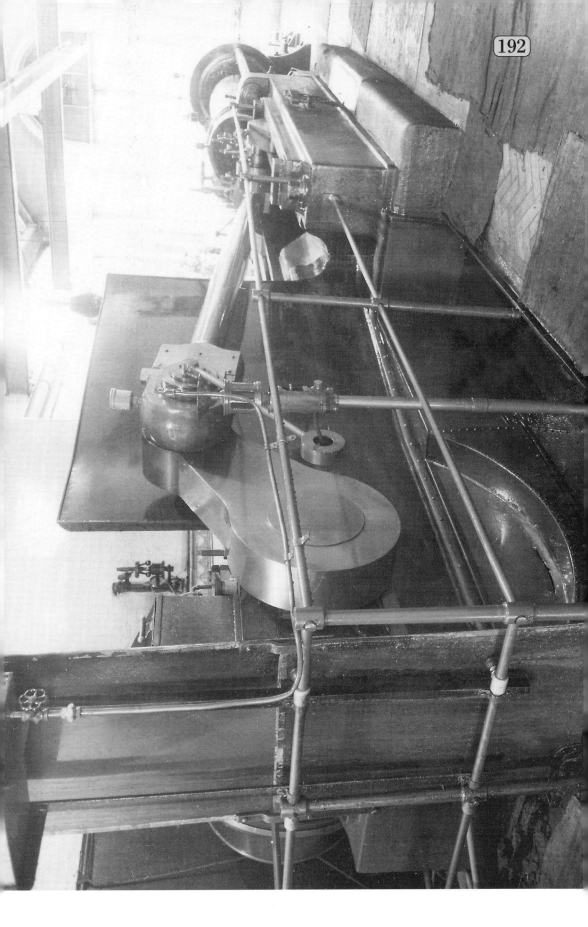

193 The Colne Vale Dye & Chemical Co., Slathwaite   SER 1238

Type:	Horizontal single cylinder condensing.
Photo taken:	1966
Maker and Date:	Maker and date unknown.
Cylinder/dimensions:	13$\frac{1}{2}$in x 2ft 0in – slide valve.
Hp: 60	*Rpm:* 100 *Psi:* 100
Service:	Works drive. 8in belt off. 3ft 9in pulley.

There were several engines driving parts of the plant which produced textile dyes, but latterly this was the main power source for the dye making section. It was a plain nondescript little engine, well made and designed, which ran with great reliability, as needed. There was nothing at all to suggest a possible maker, who would have been one of the small foundry and engineer shops which were very widespread in the valleys. It was still at work in 1973. One other engine was equally nondescript and reliable and the other was Dutch.

194 South Kirby Colliery   SER 629

Type:	Double cylinder vertical – Non-condensing.
Photo taken:	1954
Maker and Date:	Markham & Co. Chesterfield. About 1892.
Cylinder/dimensions:	42in x 6ft 0in – drop valves.
Hp:	*Rpm:* 30 *Psi:*
Service:	Coal winding. Rope drum 18ft to 30ft diameter.

This was unusual in that the vertical supporting members were rolled steel joists and not the usual cast-iron square columns, and braces. Reversing was by Stephenson's link motion. The steam valve lay-out was unusual as the inlet and exhaust valves were upon the opposite sides of the cylinder barrels, whereas most verticals had needed little attention in over 60 years of heavy work. The steam plant, and possibly the whole colliery, was gone by 1965.

195 Clay and Horsfalls, Wharf Mill, Sowerby Bridge   SER 569

Type:	Horizontal tandem compound condensing.
Photo taken:	1953
Maker and Date:	Politt and Wigzell, Sowerby Bridge, 1910.
Cylinder/dimensions:	Not known
Hp: Approx. 450	*Rpm:* 70 *Psi:* 160
Service:	Woollen mill drive.

This was a good example of Politt's later design, fitted with drop inlet and Corliss exhaust valves, and with the condenser tandem to the low pressure cylinder on the engine room floor. The drop inlet valves were driven off a side shaft, and the exhaust valves from wrist plates operated by an eccentric on the crankshaft. The mill was converted to electrical drive in the 1950's but closed later.

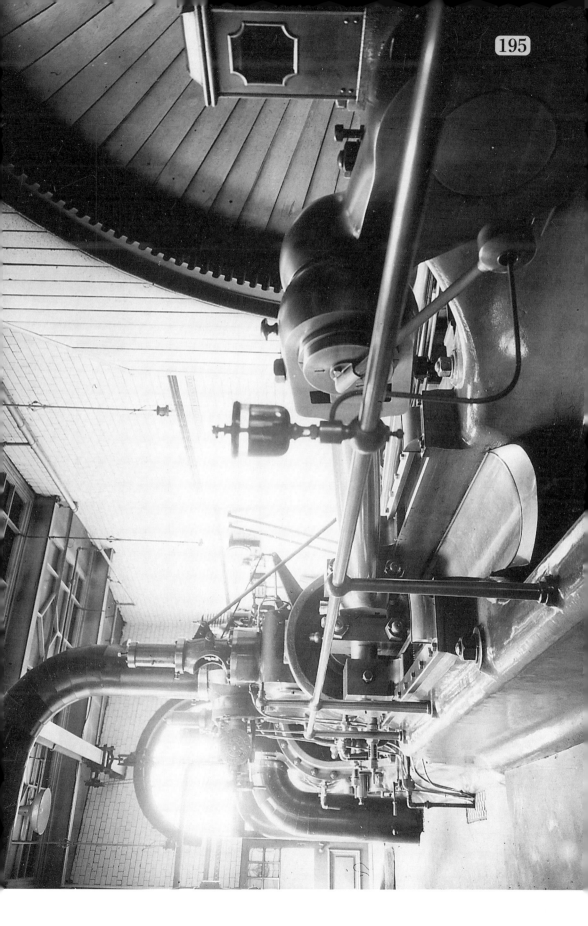

196 Shaw & Co., Stainland   SER 65

Type:	Cross Compound Beam.
Photo taken:	1936
Maker and Date:	Wood Bros., Sowerby Bridge?
Cylinder/dimensions:	24in x 42in x 6ft 0in? – Corliss valves.
Hp: Approx. 600	*Rpm:* 30 *Psi:* 140
Service:	Woollen mill, drove 5 floors, and weaving shed by two pinions from spur ring on flywheel arms.

This was believed to have been built as a double simple engine, or possibly a McNaught, and finally changed to cross compound by Wood Bros, with a pair of new cylinders. No dates or data of these changes remained however, but there is little doubt that Wood Bros., made the final change to cross compound. It had been little used since 1930. The engine house was very fine, having large figures painted on the walls at either side and with a gallery at the front of the engine room. The new mill with turbine and electric drive was built in 1930.

197 Holdsworth & Gibb, Moorside Mills, Swinton   SER 1065

Type:	Inverted vertical triple expansion.
Photo taken:	1961
Maker and Date:	Scott and Hodgson, Guide Bridge – 1895-6?
Cylinder/dimensions:	19in – 29in and 40in x 3ft 6in – Corliss and piston valves.
Hp: 850	*Rpm:* 80 *Psi:* 160
Service:	Finished cotton goods from raw cotton. 21 rope drives to mill floors.

This, a typical Scott and Hodgson triple in most ways, differed greatly in having a surface condenser which was unusual in a mill engine, and even more so in that it was made marine style, as a part of the rear columns, with a bucket type circulating pump and air pump driven from the usual levers. The mill once had four engines and much gearing, and this was a typical Scott's economy layout with a compound and the triple arranged with new rope drives to drive the whole. The compound engine drove the weaving shed, with a coupling drive which allowed it to assist the mill engine when that was overloaded, a frequent condition in the cotton trade. The drives were gradually changed over to electric motors in the 1960s, and the engines were scrapped. The middle column in the front of this engine was vertical and of forged steel; the others were of cast iron.

198 Newton Chamber Ltd, Tankersley Park Shaft   SER 67a

Type:	Inverted grasshopper non–rotative.
Photo taken:	1936
Maker and Date:	Newton Chambers Ltd., Thorncliffe Iron Works 1885
Cylinder/dimensions:	60in x 9ft 0in? – drop valves. Beam 25ft 0in long?

This again was out of use, the pits being pumped electrically. It differed from the previous engine in that the piston rod was coupled to the beam near to the pump rods at the end, the inner end of the beam swinging on a link. This still further reduced the cost since all of the effort was transferred through the beam itself, so that there was only a very slight stress at the swing link, at the inner end of the beam, and complete absence of the usual beam centre bearing. It was built non-condensing but a condenser was fitted shortly after. The steel built up beam was below with the inner end of a swing link, with the piston rod connected to it 19ft away with the pump rod attached to the outer end which projected out into the shaft. The valves were controlled by a Davey differential engine. The engine was scrapped c.1940.

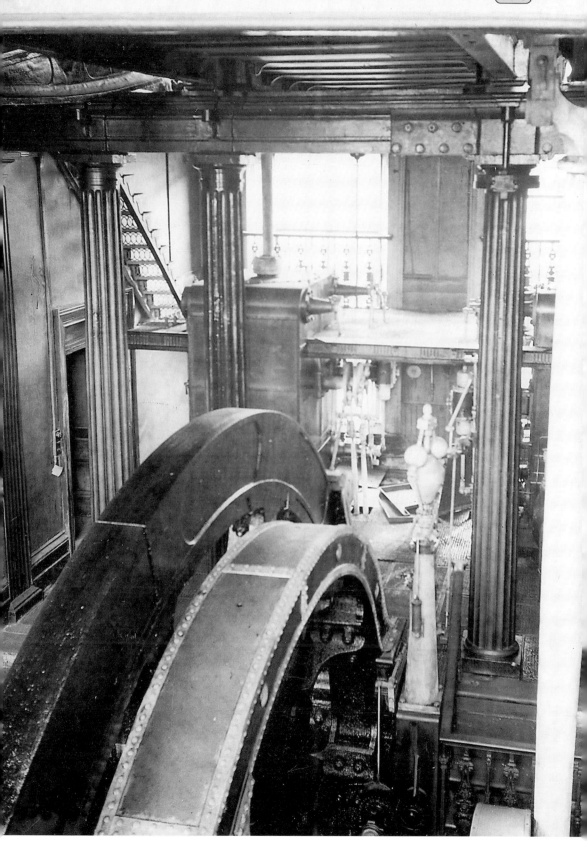

199 John Priestman Ltd. Ashfield Mills, Thornton, Bradford SER 625

Type:	Double McNaughted beam – originally Woolf compound.
Photo taken:	1953
Maker and Date:	Bowling Ironworks, 1870
Cylinder/dimensions:	28in x 3ft6in and 46in x 7ft 0in each side.
Hp: 100	*Rpm:* 22 *Psi:* 140
Service:	Woollen spinning engine.

This was built as a double 60 hp Woolf compound engine with slide valves, and was altered to McNaught-type probably by Woodhouse and Mitchell in the 1890s. It then gave the necessary additional power and ran well until, in the 1950s, all of the steam plant was scrapped, and replaced by a diesel generating plant and motor drives. There were two smaller steam engines as well as a large Hick Hargreaves cross compound engine which drove the weaving shed.

200 Nelson Bros, Millstead Mill, Todmorden   SER 1144

Type:	Horizontal single tandem
Photo taken:	1964
Maker and Date:	Wood Bros.? And Ebor Engineering Co? 1870?
Cylinder/dimensions:	14in and 28in x 3ft 6in – slide valves.
Hp: Approx.200	*Rpm:* 60 *Psi:* 120
Service:	Drive for 400 looms making many fabrics including butchers' aprons and other stripes.

The site was old in the cotton trade and beginning with a waterwheel, later had a beam engine, followed by the above engine as a single cylinder Wood Bros. possibly in the 1870s. This was later made into a tandem compound by The Ebor Co. who added the high pressure slide valve cylinder at the rear, possibly in 1898, the date of the Oldham Boiler Works boiler. The plant was usually well supplied with orders to keep part load going, but the business was closed after a fire in 1971 or 72, which destroyed the mill, although the engine and its house were saved. An interesting feature of the plant was that the engines had always driven first from a bevel wheel to the second motion shaft, owing to the layout of the site. The engine was still in position long after the fire, the remainder of the premises having been bought by a nearby concern.

201 Sandbach & Co., Calder Vale Mill, Cornholme,
Todmorden   SER 508

Type:	McNaughted single beam.
Photo taken:	1952
Maker and Date:	J. & E. Wood, Bolton? 1861. Mcnaughted 1890's?
Cylinder/dimensions:	22in x 2ft 6in 30in x 5ft 0in – slide valves.
Hp: 200	*Rpm:* 35 *Psi:* 65
Service:	Cotton weaving shed.

The rosettes moulded upon the entablature suggest that this was made by Wood Bros. of Sowerby Bridge, but nothing was known for certain of its origin. A major accident in 1900 when the beam broke led to Wm. Roberts of Nelson fitting a new beam and connecting rod, and the McNaught H.P. cylinder was also of their make. The crankshaft broke in 1950, and this was replaced by one made of Krupps steel, forged in Lancashire, and fitted in 10 days. The mill was closed and all scrapped in 1958, but their other plant at Todmorden continued at work.

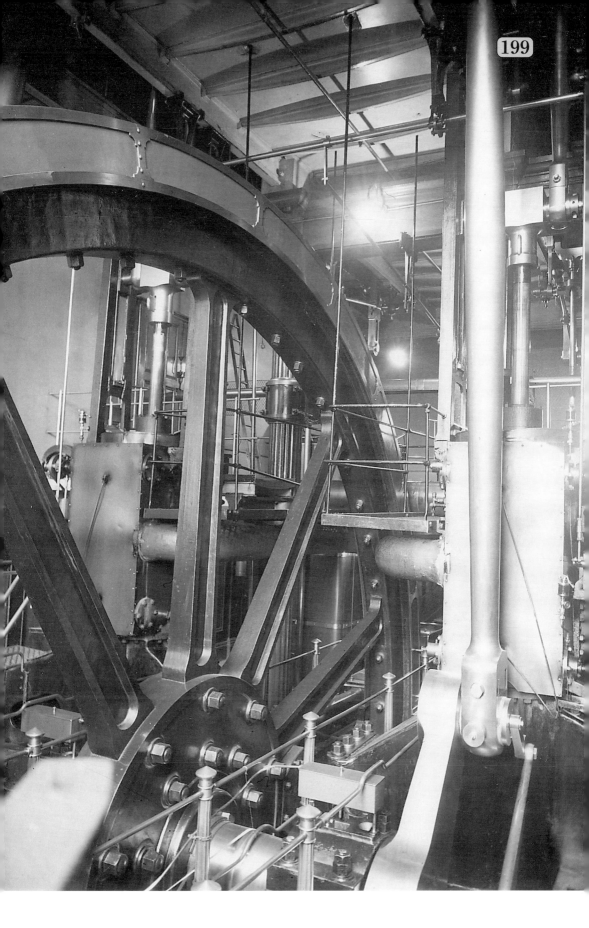

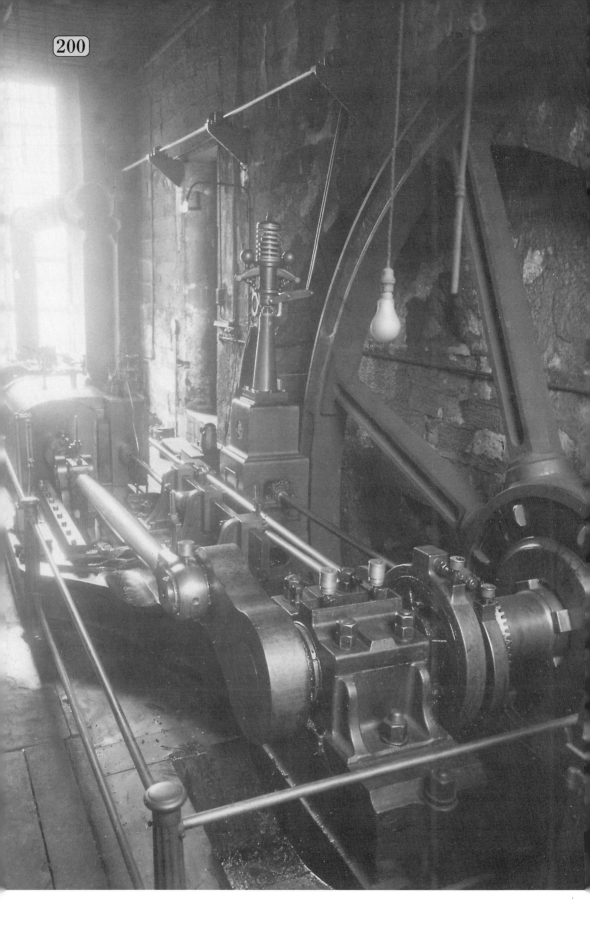

202 Lord Bros., Stacksteads Mill, Todmorden   SER 510

Type:	Horizontal cross compound.
Photo taken:	1952
Maker and Date:	J. & E. Wood, Bolton. 1867.
Cylinder/dimensions:	17^1/$_2$in & 33in x 4ft 0in Corliss valves H.P. – slide valve L.P.
Hp: 120	*Rpm:* 52 *Psi:* 60
Service:	Cotton weaving. 228 looms.

This was undoubtedly the oldest Corliss valved cylinder at work in 1950, having remained as built since 1867. It was possibly a replacement of a slide valve cylinder even then, as all of the valves were on top, whereas it was usual to place the exhaust at the bottom, which was often impossible if the original cylinder had slide valves. It drove directly from the toothed flywheel rim to a pinion upon the shed mainshaft, and driven and fired by one man. It gave very little trouble until it was scrapped about 1956, when electric drive was possibly installed, or the mill closed. Lord also made textile machinery at one time.

203 Dawson & Co., Todmorden   SER 511

Type:	Horizontal cross compound.
Photo taken:	1952
Maker and Date:	E. R. & F. Turner, Ipswich. No 2101.
Cylinder/dimensions:	9in & 16in x 1ft 6in – semi rotary valves.
Hp: 35	*Rpm:* 95 *Psi:* 100
Service:	Taping machine drive for weaving shed.

This was purchased secondhand, and installed in 1939. Taping was the operation of passing the warp or longitudinal threads of a fabric through a bath of paste, or size made of tallow, starch etc., to add to the resistance of the threads against the friction of passing through the loom in weaving. Once started it had to continue until the entire length of warp was finished, since after sizing, it passed over steam heated rollers and was dried before it was wound upon the roll (called a beam) ready to go on to the loom. Taping was therefore continued throughout the day even when the mill engine stopped at mid-day, and such engines as this, called "taping donkeys", were installed to run on during the midday stop, the exhaust often being used for the drying. Donkeys were very plain as a rule, and very rarely of this high quality.

204 Messrs. Temperleys Earthenware Pipe Manufacturer,
Todmorden   SER 550

Type:	Horizontal single tandem condensing.
Photo taken:	1953
Maker and Date:	Unknown. Altered 1900.
Cylinder/dimensions:	18in and 36in x 5ft 0in.
Hp: 350	*Rpm:* 70 *Psi:* 100
Service:	Drove clay grinding and tempering mills.

This was built as a slide valve tandem, and altered by Wood Bros., Sowerby Bridge in 1900, when the Corliss high pressure and slide valve low pressure were fitted by them. The main drive was by belt off the flywheel rim. Temperleys had three plants up the Bacup Road, all steam driven until 1950, when one after the other they were converted to motor drives and the steam plant scrapped. All of the drives were heavy and variable. The Corliss valves for the high pressure cylinder were all fitted at the top, it was a common difficulty with replacing slide valve cylinders that there was no room for the exhaust valves to be placed below.

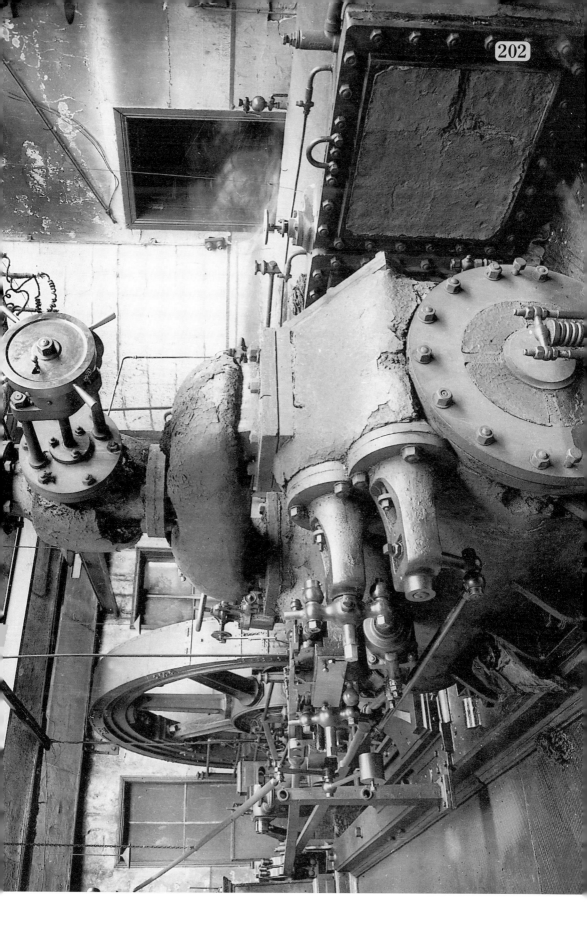

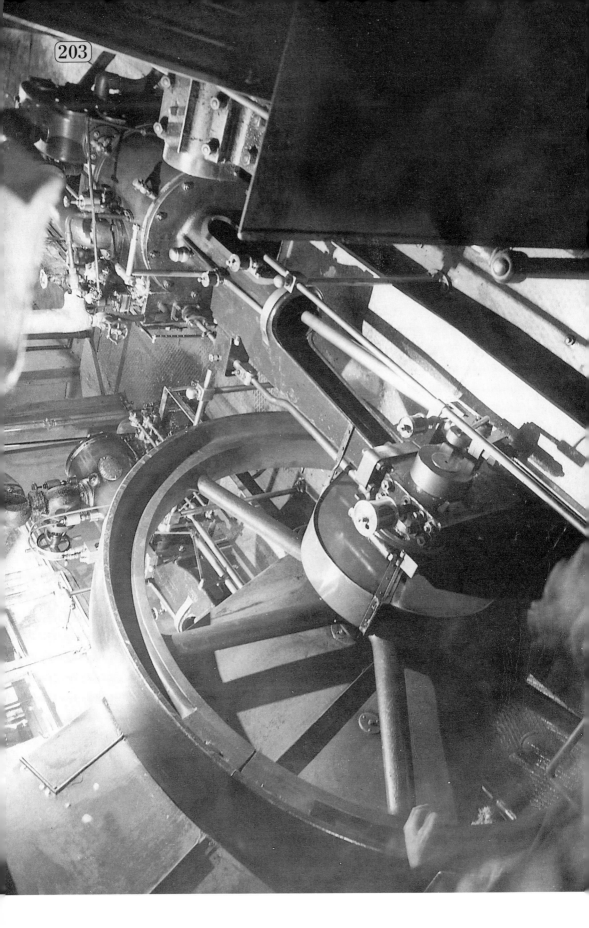

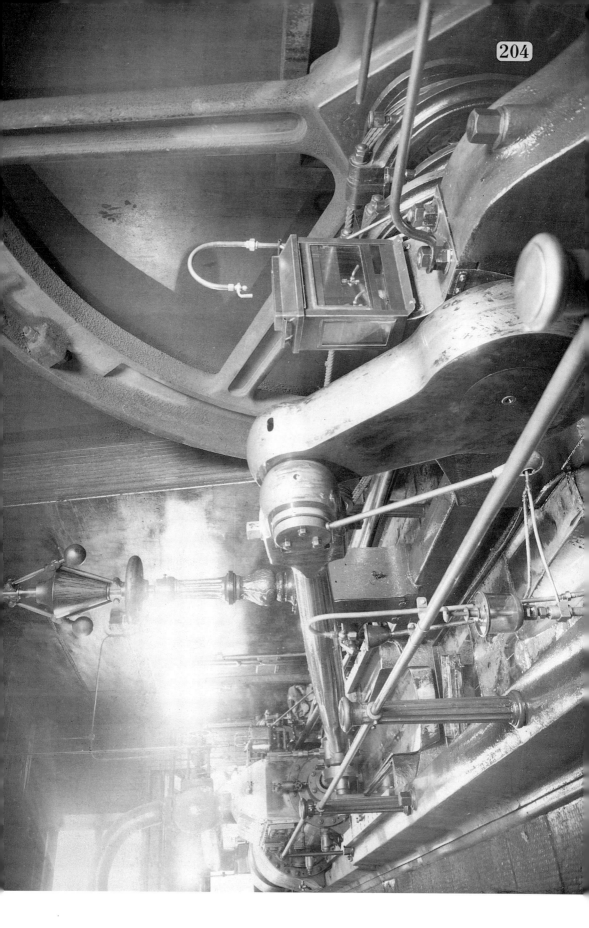

205 Fielden Bros, Waterside Mill, Todmorden   SER 61

Type:	McNaught Double Beam
Photo taken:	1936
Maker and Date:	Clayton & Goodfellow, Blackburn, 1896.
Cylinder/dimensions:	2 x 28in x 3ft 6in, 2 x 50in x 7ft 0in – slide valves.
Hp: 800	*Rpm:* 28 *Psi:* 105
Service:	Cotton weaving, Internal spur rim drive to twin sheds one at either side.
	Beams 21ft 0in long Flywheel 28ft 0in diameter.

Fieldens were originally spinners and weavers, but the spinning was discontinued, after a fire at one of the spinning plants. There were two sheds at Waterside, each of which had its own engine until the above engine was installed. The first shed was built in 1828, and was replaced by a combined spinning plant in 1889, with a new shed. The dates are not exact, but the double beam was certainly installed to drive the old and new sheds in 1896. It was a unique layout in that the drive was taken from the fly-wheel rim by internal teeth, with a separate pinion to work either side, since the mainshaft could not cross the flywheel. The old engine was stopped and the erectors worked day and night to get going in 12 weeks.

206 Fielden Bros, Waterside Mill, Todmorden   SER 61a

Type:	Internal tooth main drive gears.
Photo taken:	1936
Maker and Date:	Clayton and Goodfellow, 1896
Cylinder/dimensions:	
Hp:	*Rpm:* *Psi:*
Service:	Internal tooth main drive. Flywheel rim 28ft 0in diameter; spur pinion wheels 7ft 0in and 8ft 0in diameter.

This was virtually noiseless, possibly because the flywheel rim gear sectors were of steel. It was the quietest gear drive of the power I ever met, and this was partly due to the internal teeth. It ran perfectly when, at the closure, it was 67 years old, mostly fully loaded. Since the engine had slide valves it was very quiet; outstanding for a gear drive.

207 John Stott and Son, Der St. Mill. Todmorden   SER 621

Type:	Inverted vertical single tandem compound.
Photo taken:	1953
Maker and Date:	Wood Bros. Sowerby Bridge. Date unknown.
Cylinder/dimensions:	11in and 22in x 2ft 6in – Corliss and slide valves.
Hp: 200	*Rpm:* 90 *Psi:* 100
Service:	Cotton weaving. Rope main drive, bevel wheels to loom shafts.

The Company was started in 1862, originally with a beam engine, which was replaced by this engine which came second-hand from a mill in the Craggs Valley about 1919. Single vertical tandems were rare, but this fitted very well into the old engine room. The Meyer valve on the low pressure cylinder, with adjustable cut-off, was an unusual feature. It was named *John Thomas*, which may have related to the original owners. All was scrapped at the closure.

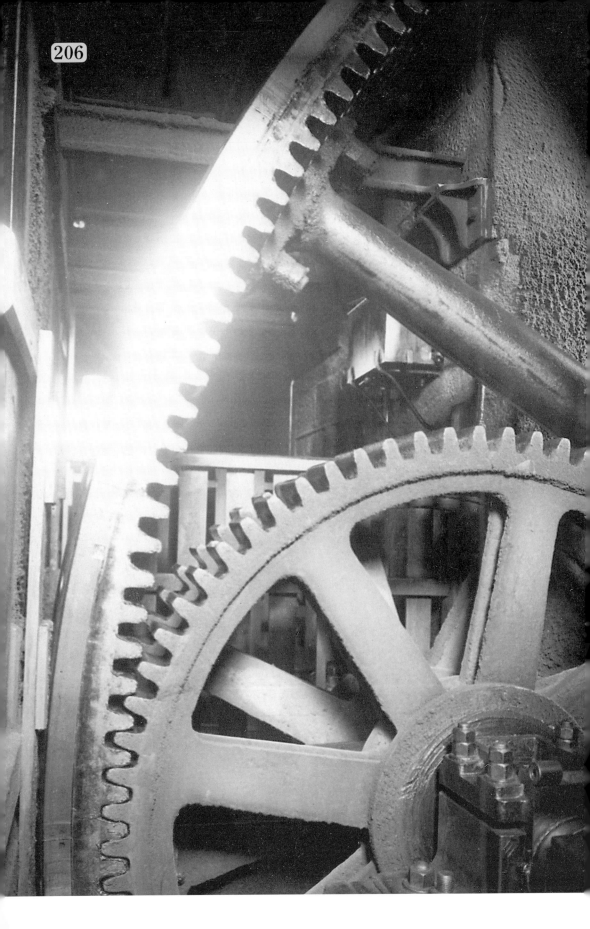

208 The Joint Stock Co., Todmorden   SER 623

Type:	Horizontal cross compound condensing.
Photo taken:	1953
Maker and Date:	The Ebor Engineering Co., Littleborough 1896.
Cylinder/dimensions:	18in and 34in x 4ft 0in – Corliss and slide valves.
Hp: 350	*Rpm:* 40 *Psi:* 100
Service:	Cotton weaving. Gear drive.

The engine and shed generally were very good, but the main gear drive from the fly was notorious as being one of the noisiest in the trade, and all attempts to reduce the nuisance and vibration failed. It was replaced by a diesel engined generating set and motors on the mainshafts, but after much trouble with the diesel engine, the mill was closed in the early 1960s when the weaving trade fell off.

209 *Woodhouse Mill, Todmorden, Lancs*   SER 69

Type:	McNaughted single beam.
Photo taken:	1936
Maker and Date:	Wood Bros. Sowerby Bridge, c 1830
Cylinder/dimensions:	$25^3/_4$in x 3ft 2in, 39in x 6ft 0in – slide valves,
Hp: 250	*Rpm:* $36^1/_2$ *Psi:* 82
Service:	Woollen spinning. Fine stone buildings, Was gear drive later converted to ropes. Engine house separate to mill with drive shaft across mill yard.
	Beam 20ft 0in long. Flywheel 24ft 0in.

A typical heavy Yorkshire engine, this ran unaltered until the 1870s when the flywheel failed; the engine was McNaughted at the same time as the new wheel was fitted. The crankshaft cracked in 1900, and the H.P. cylinder was linered at the time. Extensive other replacements were then made. The main gear driving wheel broke in 1903; it was segmental; the new one was cast in one piece, and ran very quietly. A new governor was fitted in 1914, and the last major change came in 1925, when £2,000 was spent converting the whole to rope drives. The vertical shaft and bevel wheels were removed, and the shafts rearranged to give the necessary long drive centres for the ropes. This was an immense improvement, and it was regrettable that the mill ran for only a few years after the conversion, closing in about 1930. The engine was scrapped in c.1939.

210 *Dawson & Co., Todmorden*   SER 928

Type:	Horizontal single tandem.
Photo taken:	1958
Maker and Date:	Woodhouse and Mitchell, Brighouse. 1913.
Cylinder/dimensions:	14in and 26in x 3ft 0in – Corliss valves.
Hp: 250	*Rpm:* 80 *Psi:* 120
Service:	Cotton weaving.

This was built to develop 250 hp, and ran thus until 1934, when increasing load needed more power, and a new low pressure cylinder of 28 in bore was fitted to raise the power to 300 hp The drives were all by ropes originally, but latterly (1936) some were changed over to bevel wheels, which, although secondhand, worked very well until the change to electric drives in 1958. The mill did its own yarn taping and sizing, and there was a small Turner Pegg (Ipswich) engine to drive the taping machines when the engine was stopped at mid-day. Very little had altered, except the larger low pressure cylinder, and was still highly efficient when it was superseded, later being broken up as scrap.

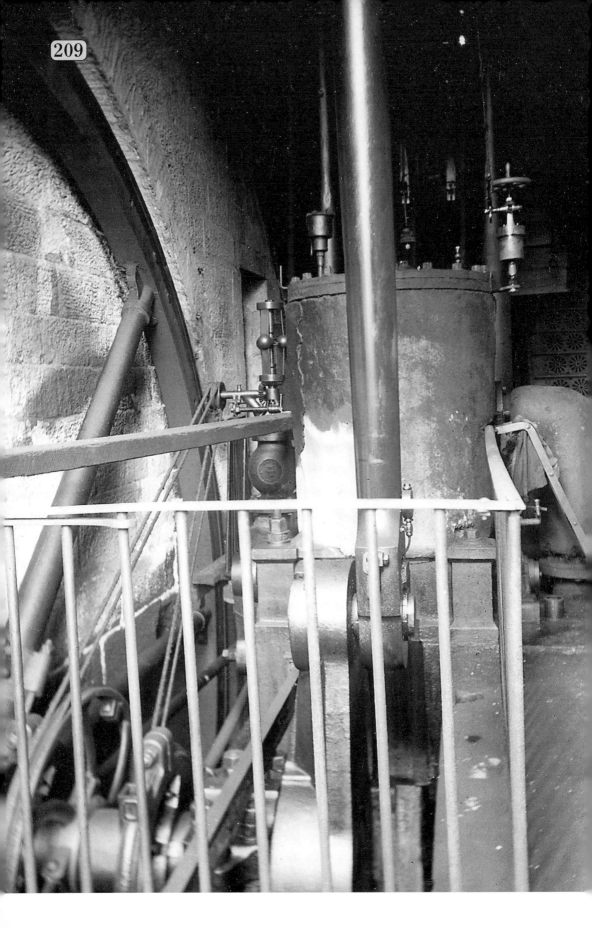

209

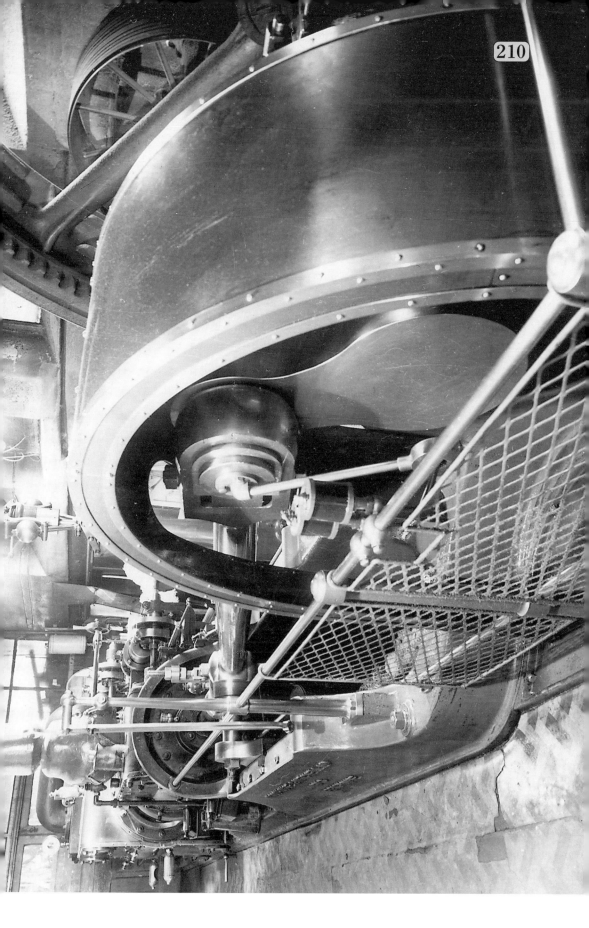

211 Ackton Hall Colliery, Nr. Wakefield, Yorks   SER 1341

Type:	Horizontal double cylinder.
Photo taken:	1968
Maker and Date:	Bradley & Craven. Wakefield 1893.
Cylinder/dimensions:	32in x 5ft 0in – Cornish valves.
Hp: ?	*Rpm:* 45 *Psi:* 100
Service:	Coal winding. Shaft 440 yds. deep. Rope drum 17ft. diameter.

Ackton Hall was a well managed pit, which had one of the first Parson's turbines used for electricity generation in a colliery. This engine was the main coal drawing unit and may have had new cylinders but otherwise, except for safety fittings, was as built, except for the possible addition of metallic piston and valve rod packings. No governor or expansion gear was fitted, but in full working it made up to 75 winds per hour with a payload of $2^{1}/_{2}$ – 3 tons of coal in a winding time of 32 seconds. The colliery was fully self contained in its heyday, with mixed pressure turbo-generators and air compressors and a steam driven fan. For all this, there were 14 Lancashire boilers installed. Coal winning ceased in the early 1960s, the reserves being nearly worked out. The early Parson's steam turbine, installed about 1893, should certainly have been preserved, but its fate is not known. All the other plant was scrapped.

212 Walton Colliery, Nr. Wakefield   SER 1345

Type:	Double cylinder horizontal.
Photo taken:	1968
Maker and Date:	John Fowler & Sons, Leeds. 1893.
Cylinder/dimensions:	42in x 7ft 0in – piston valves.
Hp: ?	*Rpm:* 40 *Psi:* 80
Service:	Coal winding. Shaft 365 yds deep. Rope drum 17ft 6in diam.

This was probably the first engine installed when the pit was sunk, and until 1922 there was only the one shaft, as the colliery was connected to the Hall Park pit as a second shaft. There were 3 decks to the cages and up to 58 winding runs in coal turning were made per hour, with a payload of 2 tons 15cwt. of coal each. It was very unusual for a winder, in that internal piston type cut off valves were fitted inside the main piston valves, which had a separate set of link motion to drive them, so that there were four sets of Stephenson's link motion to the engine, a very rare feature. It had not been altered as far as could be seen, although the drum was renewed as were many of the cast iron end plated ones, as the metal became brittle. The other engine was a Robey about 1935. The whole pit was due to be closed in the early 1970s.

213 Caphouse Colliery, Overton, Nr. Wakefield   SER 1410

Type:	Double cylinder horizontal.
Photo taken:	1970
Maker and Date:	Davy Bros. Sheffield. 1876
Cylinder/dimensions:	16in x 3ft 0in – slide valves.
Hp: ?	*Rpm:* 60 *Psi:* 80
Service:	Coal winding. Shaft 150 yds deep. Rope drum 9ft diameter.

The colliery was sunk by E.L.Kaye, (whose initials are carved in the engine house wall) in 1876 and the engine was new then. The timber headgear and the engine, except for added safety gear and metallic packings served through the life of the colliery (some 90 years) until the closure in 1970 or so. It was a happy pit, with a good output of a coal readily sold in the area. The winding was very fast with the small rope drum, making the wind of $14^{1}/_{2}$ revolutions in 15 seconds, latterly with 8 cwt of coal per wind, but it was less than this for much of its life. There were two Lancashire boilers, and the engine like the rest, was a model of simple efficiency. The pit closed probably owing to the distance of underground haulage.

214 Shuttle Eye Colliery, Nr, Wakefield   SER 1455

Type:	Double cylinder horizontal
Photo taken:	1973
Maker and Date:	Bradley & Craven, Wakefield. 1930.
Cylinder/dimensions:	22in x 3ft 6in – drop and Corliss valves.
Hp: ?	*Rpm:* 40 *Psi:* 120
Service:	Coal winding. Shaft 185 yds deep. Rope drum 12ft. diameter.

One shaft was converted to electric winding in the early 1960s, and this one then became the men and material shaft. It was almost certainly the last new steam winding engine to be installed in the area, but nothing was known of the previous engines at the site. The engine was Bradley's latest type, with fixed cut-off, drop inlet and Corliss exhaust valves, driven from a wrist plate. The drum was supported by a cast iron spider with tee section arms at the ends, and in the middle by a simple "L" section ring, without arms. The colliery was closed in 1973 as the coal seams were becoming too thin (as small as 21 inches thick) to work economically, and most of the plant would be scrapped. There were three Lancashire boilers, two of 9ft 6in diameter, but there were more when the small power house and steam driven fan were in operation.

215 Aire & Calder Navigation Co., Ryehill, Nr. Wakefield   SER 380a

Type:	Cornish beam.
Photo taken:	1951
Maker and Date:	Harvey & Co., Hayle 1864.
Cylinder/dimensions:	50in x 8ft 0in.
Hp:	*Rpm:* 6–8 *Psi:* 50–60
Service:	Canal water supply.

This was built for Tremenhere Mine, Cornwall, costing £1,025 with two boilers, and was sold to the Aire & Calder Co., in 1875, after the mine closed. The price was then £915 with doors and window frames, the removal to Penrhyn and Goole then costing £220. A new boiler by J Clayton, Leeds was supplied in 1935, otherwise little was altered except that for the low canal lift, a large plunger pump replaced the mine pitwork. It was originally a well finished engine, of usual design. The whole was demolished about l963.

216 Aire & Calder Navigation, Ryehill, Wakefield   SER 380b

Type:	Plunger pump.
Photo taken:	1951
Maker and Date:	
Cylinder/dimensions:	60in diameter x 8ft 0in.
Hp:	*Rpm:* *Psi:*
Service:	Low lift pump. Canal water supply.

The engine supplied water to the top pound of the lock system and high level section, possibly 25ft 0in head, but with plant standing this was uncertain.

215

217 *Wath Main Colliery* SER 628

Type:	Inverted vertical double cylinders.
Photo taken:	1954
Maker and Date:	Bradley and Craven, Wakefield, 1926
Cylinder/dimensions:	38in x 5ft 0in – drop valves.
Hp: ?	*Rpm:* 30 *Psi:* 120
Service:	Coal winding. Shaft 1800 ft deep. Rope drum 17ft 0in diameter.

Inverted vertical winding engines, i.e. with the cylinders at the top were uncommon in winding, and this was perhaps adopted here to save space and possibly cost of foundations, and it probably replaced an old vertical engine in the same space. The new engine house was a very ugly concrete structure, and the original wooden headgear was still retained in the 1950s, despite the greatly increased capacity of the new engine. The governor controlled cut-off was still used giving high economy in the 1950s. The colliery was probably closed in the re-organisation of the collieries, and all scrapped.

218 *Denisons Ltd., Ling Bob, Nr. Wilsden* SER 64

Type:	McNaughted single beam.
Photo taken:	1936
Maker and Date:	Bowling Ironworks, Bradford, 1850?
Cylinder/dimensions:	18 in x 1ft 6in, 21in x 3ft 0in – slide valves.
Hp: Approx. 75	*Rpm:* 50 *Psi:* 14ft 0in
Service:	Cloth processing, was gear drive off flywheel arms to pinion on mill shaft, later replaced by rope drive, so that the engine ran wrong way round. Beam 10ft 6in long. Flywheel 14ft 0in diameter.

This was certainly at work for over a century and was probably McNaughted in 1890, when no doubt the rope drive was installed. It ran 16 hours daily for the last 30 years of its life and was working perfectly when a fire near it caused damage by water on the heated engine. It ran virtually unattended only getting occasional oiling. With the rope drive it was very quiet, almost soundless in fact.

219 *Wombwell Main Colliery, South Yorkshire* SER 385a

Type:	Two vertical twin cylinder non–condensing.
Photo taken:	1951
Maker and Date:	J. Musgrave & Sons, Bolton 1853.
Cylinder/dimensions:	30in x 5ft 0in – drop valves.
Hp:	*Rpm:* 25–30 *Psi:* 50–60
Service:	Coal winding.

Most of the vertical winding engines were fitted with twin cylinders and were faster and more easily handled than the singles and this was one of the first three engines of the type made by Musgraves. No positive history could be established, but new cylinders for higher pressure were fitted later, and the placing of the valve gear between the rope reels suggest that it was originally similar to the Durham form, and converted to link motion later. The crankshafts were supported by solid brick walls, with neat slide bars built into the structure.

220 *Wombwell Main Colliery, near Barnsley* SER 385b

Type:	Reels for flat ropes.
Photo taken:	1951
Maker and Date:	
Cylinder/dimensions:	Diameter 13ft 0in Flywheel 18ft 0in diameter.
Hp:	*Rpm:* *Psi:*
Service:	Coal winding.

The two engines were built to use flat hemp ropes, but one was converted to a drum using round ropes about 1900. The illustration shows the reel structure, consisting of a narrow rim with horns or side arms to guide the coils of the rope to wind upon each other, in contrast to the drum where the coils of the round rope wound on side by side. It was extremely rare for round ropes to coil upon each other due to the risk of damage by crushing.

221 *James Ives and Co., Leafield Mill, Yeadon, Yorks.* SER 1236

Type:	Horizontal single tandem.
Photo taken:	1966
Maker and Date:	Pollit and Wigzell 1903.
Cylinder/dimensions:	15in and 24in x 4ft 0in.
Hp: 250	*Rpm:* 77 *Psi:* 120
Service:	Mill drive. 12 ropes off 14ft. flywheel. Mainly to alternators latterly.

This was virtually as built except for the fitting of a Lumb governor, and in the 1960s the Pollit & Wigzell rounded edge crank was replaced by a plain slab one, the first instance I ever met of this being done on a Pollit & Wigzell engine. The deep main bed was reduced where the cylinders were fitted, otherwise it was all that a Politt & Wigzell was expected to be. It was still running in the 1970s.

SERIES EDITOR, TONY WOOLRICH

Tony was born in Bristol in 1938. He became interested in technical history in his school days, and has been a Member of the Newcomen Society for 40 years, for ten years of which serving as a sub-editor of the *Newcomen Transactions*. He is also a Member of SHOT (the Society for the History of Technology), ICOHTEC (the International Committee for the History of Technology) and the Somerset Archaeological and Natural History Society.

He trained as a craftsman in the engineering industry, and from 1970 has combined his craft and historical skills in modelmaking for museums and heritage projects.

He has also published books and articles on aspects of technical history and biography. A particular interest is industrial espionage of the 18th century. Another interest is 18th century and early 19th century technical books and encyclopaedias, in particular Rees's *Cyclopædia*, (1802-1819). He has been working on a biography of the engineer John Farey, jr (1791-1851) for the past 20 years.

Since 1989 he has been heavily involved cataloguing for the National Monuments Record, Swindon, the Watkins Collection on the Stationary Steam Engine. He is also a constant consultee to the Monuments Protection Programme of English Heritage.

Since 1994 he has been acting as a contributor to the New *Dictionary of National Biography* working on biographies of engineers and industrialists. He is a contributor to the forthcoming *Biographical Dictionary of Civil Engineers,* published by the Institution of Civil Engineers

He has recently completed for Wessex Water plc a study of the water supplies of Bridgwater, Wellington (Somerset) and Taunton, and was part of the team setting up the company's education centres at Ashford (near Bridgwater) and Sutton Poyntz (near Weymouth).

ENGINE MAKERS INDEX

Maker	SER Nº	Page Nº
Farland & Brearley	63	26
Fowler, J	1345	212
Fraser & Chalmers	1429	44
Fraser & Chalmers	1430	45
Galloway, W & J	694	33
Galloway, W & J	989a	131
Galloway, W & J	989c	132
Galloway, W & J	993a	156
Galloway, W & J	1045	130
Garrett	1023	96
Gledhill, R & J	273	86
Glenfield & Kennedy (?)	1343	107
Harveys of Hayle	380a	215
Hathorn, Davey	1078	144
Hick, Hargreaves	1039a	152
Hick, Hargreaves	1129	105
Hick, Hargreaves	1155	1
Hick, Hargreaves	1500	113
Horsfield, J & J	111	10
Hoyle & Son	151	114
Kilburns	1386	73
King & Menzies	150	91
Kitson & Co	114	164
Lamberton & Co	733c	158
Lamberton & Co	1073	167
Lilleshall Co	627	151
Low Moor Ironworks	269	23
Mare & Co	187	161
Markham & Co	629	194
Markham & Co	630	9
Markham & Co	733d	160
Markham & Co	733d	157
Markham & Co	1411	76
Marsden's Engines	693	136
Marsden's Engines	1001	147
Marsden's Engines	1111	39
Marsden's Engines	1342	40
Marsden's Engines	1401	137
Marsden's Engines	1468	138
Mark Shaw	1138	16
McNaught, J & W	1348	188
Mills, E	1491b	111
Musgrave, J	385a	218
Musgrave, J	1428a	41
Newton, Bean & Mitchell	926	75
Newton, Bean & Mitchell	931	49
Newton, Bean & Mitchell	1088	57
Newton, Bean & Mitchell	1235	106
Newton, Bean & Mitchell	1351	148
Newton, Chambers	66a	31
Newton, Chambers	66b	32
Newton, Chambers	67a	198

Maker	SER Nº	Page Nº
Newton, Chambers	67b	47
Pollit & Wigzell	57a	125
Pollit & Wigzell	552	66
Pollit & Wigzell	569	195
Pollit & Wigzell	697	120
Pollit & Wigzell	805	27
Pollit & Wigzell	1059	52
Pollit & Wigzell	1060	56
Pollit & Wigzell	1066a	97
Pollit & Wigzell	1087	18
Pollit & Wigzell	1088	34
Pollit & Wigzell	1089	58
Pollit & Wigzell	1091	78
Pollit & Wigzell, (Reblt)	1188	100
Pollit & Wigzell	1236	221
Rhodes, J	357	179
Roberts, Wm	1186a	4
Schofield & Taylor	1237	186
Scott & Hodgson	619a	70
Scott & Hodgson	1065	197
Scott & Hodgson	1150	190
Shaw, M	1074	192
Smith Bros & Eastwood	1105	99
Sturges, J	270a	24
Sulzer Bros	1191	21
Taylor	58	162
Taylor & Hirst	109a	36
Thompson & Stather	379a	92
Thornewill & Wareham	1168	168
Tod Bros	1084	139
Turner, E R & F	511	203
Unknown	60	68
Unknown	106a	53
Unknown	108	55
Unknown	109b	37
Unknown	152	11
Unknown	152b	12
Unknown	182	115
Unknown	270b	25
Unknown	275	50
Unknown	276	80
Unknown	277	87
Unknown	278	82
Unknown	356b	177
Unknown	359	7
Unknown	383b	182
Unknown	550	204
Unknown	617	69
Unknown	692	134
Unknown	692	135
Unknown	840	121

Maker	SER N°	Page N°
Unknown	1044b	129
Unknown	1069a	28
Unknown	1090	127
Unknown	1152	187
Unknown	1166b	15
Unknown	1238	193
Unknown	1402	85
Unknown	1428b	42
Unknown	1491a	110
Various	1428c	43
Walker Bros	1222	30
Walker Bros	1344	146
Walker, Eaton	255	174
Walker, Eaton	336	176
Watt, James	888	94
Watt, James	1079	145
Whitham, S & J	183	116
Whitworth & Co	57	126
Willans Siemens	379 b	93
Wood Bros	65	195
Wood Bros	69	209
Wood Bros	381	64
Wood Bros	551	65
Wood Bros	880	83
Wood Bros	929	72
Wood Bros	997	150
Wood Bros	1232	74
Wood Bros? / Ebor Eng	1144	200
Woodhouse & Mitchell	928	210
Woodhouse & Mitchell	1112a	103
Woodhouse & Mitchell	1112b	104
Woodhouse & Mitchell	1130	149
Woodhouse & Mitchell	1234	48
Wood, J & E	508	201
Wood, J & E	510	202
Wood, J & E	619a	71
Wood, J & E	1490	122
Wood, J	367	63
Wood, Baldwin	1346	108
Wood, Baldwin	1349	84
Wood, Baldwin	1492	112
Wood Bros	59	67
Wood Bros	105	51
Wood Bros	621	207
Wood Bros	1154	185
Worthington Simpson	733f	161
Yates & Thom	1039b	153
Yates & Thom	1431	46
Yates, W & J	990	95
Yates, W & J	1108	19

NON-STEAM ENGINE INDEX

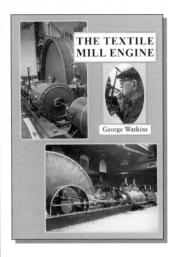

THE TEXTILE MILL ENGINE

By George Watkins

Produced in the same format, including over
150 plates of engines.

Formerly produced as two volumes, these are now published together.
The engines are cross-indexed to both engine types and makers
By and large, these photographs will not appear in
Stationary Steam Engines of Gt Britain

N.B. Stocks of this book are now limited.
232pp paperback £22.50
ISBN: 1 901522 43 1

Full details upon request

LANDMARK
Publishing Ltd ••••

Waterloo House, 12 Compton, Ashbourne, Derbyshire DE6 1DA England
Tel 01335 347349 Fax 01335 347303
e-mail landmark@clara.net web site: www.landmarkpublishing.co.uk